FOOD SCIENCE

The Biochemistry of Food and Nutrition

Teacher's Resource Guide

Third Edition

Kay Yockey Mehas
Home Economics Teacher
Curriculum Coordinator/Principal
Eugene, Oregon

Sharon Lesley Rodgers
Chemistry Teacher
Henry D. Sheldon High School
Eugene, Oregon

GLENCOE
McGraw-Hill

New York, New York   Columbus, Ohio   Mission Hills, California   Peoria, Illinois

Glencoe/McGraw-Hill

A Division of The McGraw·Hill Companies

Send all inquiries to:
Glencoe/McGraw-Hill
3008 West Willow Knolls Drive
Peoria, IL 61614-1083

ISBN: 0-02-647656-8 (Teacher's Resource Guide)
ISBN: 0-02-647647-9 (Student Edition)
ISBN: 0-02-647648-7 (Student Activity Workbook)

2 3 4 5 6 7 8 9   DBH   00 99 98 97

Table of Contents

Teaching with Food Science

Food science is an integrated approach subject that is defined as the science of the production, processing, preparation, evaluation, and utilization of food. Individuals with backgrounds in chemistry, microbiology, home economics, nutrition, engineering, quality control, dietetics, and various research specialties can all be found working in the field of food science.

Nutrition is the scientific understanding of how food is used by the body. Much of the work in food science is directed toward providing people with food of the highest nutritional value. *Food Science* highlights nutrition concepts and explores the various relationships between food science and nutrition.

Food science is not the same as food preparation. Food scientists use scientific methods to conduct laboratory experiments with food. The preparation of edible food products is not the primary purpose of a food science course, although, from time to time, such products are the result of experiments performed.

Food science is an expanding field of study. The complexity of food and the changes it undergoes offer a wide array of research topics for food scientists. This course gives students some insight into the many career possibilities in the food science field.

As students progress through this course, they use the scientific method to study the biological and chemical basis of nutrition and food preparation, preservation, and processing. Students develop laboratory, writing, and critical reasoning skills through: measuring, recording, and graphing data; predicting and evaluating laboratory results; and writing laboratory reports.

WHY TEACH FOOD SCIENCE?

Food Science is a course that provides a solid foundation for students to develop the skills they will need for the twenty-first century. Here are the skills that students need for success and which are provided in this course.

1. Thinking Skills
   - Focussing: Selectively attending to information
   - Information Gathering: Becoming conscious of relevant data
   - Remembering: Storing and retrieving information
   - Comprehending: Demonstrating understanding
   - Analyzing: Examining parts and relationships
   - Generating: Producing new information/meanings and ideas
   - Integrating: Synthesizing (connecting and combining)
   - Evaluating: Assessing reasonableness and quality of ideas.
2. Physical Sensing Skills
   - Visual
   - Auditory
   - Tactile
   - Kinesthetic
3. Social Skills
   - Social Interaction Skills
   - Social Skills for Classroom/Group Work
   - Social Skills for Self-Awareness

The latest brain research tells us that students learn best when what they are studying makes sense and/or has meaning. Also, students need to connect new information with their prior knowledge and experience. Food provides the perfect foundation to study scientific principles. It is a subject that is familiar to all students. *Food Science* builds from the students' prior knowledge and provides real-world connections in all their experiments.

Research and national reports are saying schools restructuring for the twenty-first century need to provide students with authentic tasks; and encourage team work, self-esteem, and authentic assessment. *Food Science* is a perfect fit. The laboratory experiments are designed to be performed in teams; each team of two students works in a laboratory station of four students. They work together in the allocation of resources, time, and expertise. It is an automatic structure for cooperative learning lessons.

Due to the complex nature of foods, experiments are 'real life' with many unknown factors students need to consider. Experiments may vary, and students are challenged to prove the reasons why. *Food Science* provides a format that is perfect for authentic assessment opportunities. Students can help develop a rubric and then perform the laboratory experiments as an exam. Their performance is judged by a set criteria. Many students prefer this form of testing to the traditional pen and paper exam.

The goal of education is to encourage all students to be successful in life. *Food Science: The Biochemistry of Food and Nutrition* is a course that enables students to learn biological and chemical concepts, while using chemical substances that are familiar and unthreatening. The combination paves a definite pathway to success.

For this reason, *Food Science: The Biochemistry of Food and Nutrition* can be used as an excellent introductory level science course. Students have the opportunity to become familiar with laboratory equipment such as balances, graduated cylinders and burets. They develop skill at reporting experimental results in an organized manner, while learning basic chemistry and biology, which they can build on later in full year courses on these subjects.

Food science, as presented in this text, is not a heavily mathematical course. Consequently another curricular possibility is to offer food science to older students who might have difficulty in traditional chemistry or physics classes. These students can be highly successful in food science, since it presents scientific concepts in a setting with which students are familiar. At the same time, if space and staffing allow for it, highly capable students find the course interesting and enjoy the challenge of the extension activities available.

Career opportunities in food science are extensive. Taking a high school level food science course can awaken students who may not have previously given any consideration to a career in science, to the possibility of just such a career. In conclusion, *Food Science: The Biochemistry of Food and Nutrition* is a course timely in its subject matter, broad in scope, and appealing to students of all ability levels.

In addition, food science offers school administrators a way to make the best possible use of school facilities. For example, if a personal finance class is assigned to a foods laboratory, thousands of dollars worth of equipment is unused during that period. Offering food science is a way to use that equipment, increase the number of science courses available to students, and avoid further strain on what may be overloaded science facilities.

CONTRIBUTIONS OF FOOD SCIENCE TO 21ST CENTURY SCHOOLS

Benefits to Students:

- Prior knowledge base
- Experiential, hands-on class
- Authentic tasks
- Interdisciplinary/integrated class
- Solid scientific methods
- 21st century skills
- Cooperative learning format
- Many career opportunities
- Variety of assessment
- Promotes students' success
- Better consumers

Benefits to School:

- Better use of school facilities
- Inexpensive laboratory class
- Promotes public relations
- Evening-parent/student class
- Integrates blocks
- Community/mentor programs
- Fits restructured school

Benefits to Teachers:

- T.R.G. makes it easy
- Networking format
- Easy daily format
- Fewer supplies needed
- Fewer expenses
- Less shopping required
- Cooperative learning format

HOW TO SET UP A FOOD SCIENCE CURRICULUM

The first step in introducing food science into your school's curriculum is to investigate the needs of your school to determine how a food science course can help meet those needs. Next, become familiar with your district's science goals and requirements, if they exist. These should be on file at your district administrative office.

While food science will not fit neatly into any single traditional science area, the course should meet a significant number of science goals across the board. List the ways in which food science will meet the stated science goals so you can present this information to whomever is responsible for curriculum decisions. In writing your rationale and presenting it, stress that food science can be taught to meet the needs of students at any ability level—from those with limited mathematics backgrounds to those planning careers in science. The fact that the course is not an expensive one to introduce into the curriculum should be a point in its favor. Be sure to discuss your plans and hopes for adding food science to the curriculum with the appropriate administrators.

If the course is to be offered for science credit, determine how it can assist the science department to meet its goals. For example, perhaps food science can be an alternative for students needing one year of science beyond biology. Some of these students may lack sufficient mathematics skills to take chemistry. The mathematics in food science is comparable to that found in most biology courses. If science laboratory space is a problem, perhaps food science can be an alternate way for students to earn credit for a laboratory course. In your discussions with the science faculty, stress that food science is not meant to replace existing science courses, but rather to augment existing offerings while utilizing home economics personnel and facilities.

If your own science background is a bit rusty, there are several ways you can prepare yourself for teaching food science. You can, of course, simply read some of the college-level food science textbooks listed as references in this *Teacher's Resource Guide*. If there is a science teacher willing to work with you, you can begin teaching the course knowing that your colleague will assist you if any of the subject matter is confusing.

You may also wish to contact the nearest university that has a food science and technology department. Check into the possibility of university sponsorship of workshops on key concepts in food science. A summer course for high school teachers planning to teach food science is another option. University faculty in food science are generally enthusiastic about having high school students learn about food science and the opportunities in the field. Therefore, they are usually supportive of those planning to institute such programs in high schools.

Food science, as presented in *Food Science*, is an experiment-oriented course. The course addresses a significant number of science goals. Students constantly use the scientific method to gain knowledge. Food science applies both chemical and biological concepts to the study of food. This gives students who have already taken these courses an opportunity to apply their knowledge in everyday situations. On the other hand, students who have not taken biology and/or chemistry gain some knowledge in these areas. They see firsthand how these subjects apply to the study of food.

THE FOOD SCIENCE TEACHING PROGRAM

The *Food Science* teaching program includes the *Food Science* student text, a *Student Activity Workbook*, and this *Food Science Teacher's Resource Guide*. The combination of the text, the workbook, and the *Teacher's Resource Guide* will help you plan a comprehensive course that is adapted to your students' interests and abilities and to your individual teaching style.

● **The Student Text**

Food Science was written and designed to capture the interest of students. Its layout and features help students master the concepts presented.

Unit Openers

Each of the five units contains a two-page unit opener that sets the stage for the upcoming chapters. The unit openers introduce the topics that follow and help students see how the unit chapters are related to each other.

Chapter Features

Student Objectives. At the beginning of each chapter, objectives are listed. The objectives give an overview of what students can learn after reading the chapter.

Terms to Remember. Following the objectives in each chapter is a list of terms that will be introduced in the chapter. Each term is highlighted in bold-face type when first introduced and defined in the chapter text. Pronunciation guides are given for words that are difficult to pronounce.

Nutrition and You. Each chapter contains a nutrition feature entitled "Nutrition and You." This feature highlights the nutritional aspects of the topic under consideration.

Experiments. The experiments are the heart of the *Food Science* teaching program. Each chapter contains two experiments that help students apply and extend the information learned in the chapter. The experiments contain introductory material, a detailed procedure, follow-up questions for students to answer, and a sample data table. (Suggestions for multi-level use of experiments are provided in each chapter's Suggestions for Lesson Planning in the *Teacher's Resource Guide*. Look for Laboratory Simplification and Laboratory Enrichment.)

Supplementary Information. Scattered throughout each chapter are boxes which contain supplementary information. Covering a variety of topics, the material in the boxes adds interest and depth to the text content.

To Sum Up. At the end of each chapter is a chapter summary. Students can use the summary to review and check their mastery of the concepts presented in the chapter.

Check Your Facts. These questions at the end of each chapter relate directly to the facts presented in the textbook. Students will find the answers to these questions by carefully reading the text.

Critical Thinking and Problem Solving. Each chapter also contains a list of questions that call on students to think, reason, and solve problems. These questions focus on the broader applications and implications of the material presented in the chapter.

Glossary. The extensive glossary at the end of the book is a resource for the teacher and students in understanding unfamiliar terms. All "Terms to Remember" are included in the glossary. In addition, other terms whose meanings may not be known to students are contained in the glossary.

● The *Student Activity Workbook*

Each chapter of the *Student Activity Workbook* begins with a study guide that students can complete as they read through the text and later use for review. The *Workbook* also contains a wealth of hand-outs that reinforce, enrich, and extend text content. Also included are all of the experiments printed in the text; students can use these sheets for recording information during lab work.

Note that several chapters in the *Student Activity Workbook* have analogy worksheets. It is good to review the concept of analogical reasoning with your students. Analogies help students identify concepts and their relationships—a skill that will help them when taking national placement exams. The process students need to use includes these two steps:
- identify the relationship of the concepts in the first set; and
- look at the next word set and find a similar relationship.

Encourage your students to create their own analogies for the vocabulary in the test.

● The *Teacher's Resource Guide*

This *Teacher's Resource Guide* is designed to help you teach the content presented in *Food Science*. In this introductory section, you will find a suggested schedule for a 180-day course and a 90-day course. General suggestions for planning and guiding student learning are given. Films, an outside reading list, and teacher references are suggested.

Chapter Features

Suggestions for Lesson Planning. Suggestions for lesson planning are given for each chapter in the text. Each of these sections contains the following elements:
- A suggested time schedule.
- Student objectives (reprinted from text).
- Chapter summary (reprinted from text).
- Background information about the content of the chapter.

- A list of reproducible materials found in the *Teacher's Resource Guide*.
- A list of suggested classroom activities.
- A list of extension activities for more advanced students.
- An overview of each experiment that includes the time needed to complete the experiment, the objective of the experiment, the equipment and supplies needed for the experiment, helpful hints for conducting the experiment, and information on the data you can expect students to obtain.
- An answer key that contains answers to "Nutrition and You," "Check Your Facts," "Critical Thinking and Problem Solving," the chapter "Study Guide," other chapter handouts, and the questions.

Reproducible Pages. Each chapter contains several pages which can be reproduced for your use or that of your students:
- A transparency that can be used during discussion with students.
- Complete extension experiments are included in some chapters to provide additional laboratory experiences for students. These are labeled with the chapter numbers and letters. The extension experiments from Chapter 1 are **Experiment 1-A** and **Experiment 1-B**. By duplicating the experiments from the *Teacher's Resource Guide*, you can provide students with all the necessary information so they will not need to take their textbooks into the laboratories as they conduct the experiments.

A SUGGESTED SCHEDULE FOR TEACHING FOOD SCIENCE

Food Science can be utilized as either a full-year or a one-semester course. Listed below are the suggested number of days to spend on each chapter for a course of either length.

Chapter	180-Day Course	90-Day Course
1. What Is Food Science?	6	4
2. The Scientific Evaluation of Food	8	4
3. Basic Science for Food Scientists	8	5
4. Energy	9	5
5. Acids and Bases	7	4
6. Water	8	3
7. Carbohydrates	10	5
8. Lipids	8	4
9. Protein	9	3
10. Vitamins and Minerals	8	4
11. Metabolism	9	4
12. Enzymes	9	4
13. Solutions, Colloidal Dispersions, and Emulsions	8	4
14. Leavening Agents and Baked Goods	8	4
15. Fermentation and Food	9	4
16. Dairy Products and Processing	8	4
17. Food Safety	9	4
18. Dehydration	6	4
19. Canning	6	3
20. New Techniques of Food Preservation	6	2
21. Additives	8	6
22. Developing Experiments in Food Science	9	4
23. Careers	4	2

These suggested time schedules are guidelines only. Each teacher will want to adapt and adjust the schedule to fit the particular needs and interests of the students taught.

In general, if a 90-day course is taught, there will be time for students to conduct only one experiment from each chapter. It will probably be necessary to eliminate the guest speakers and most of the films. It may also be more practical to test at the end of each unit, rather than after every chapter. As an alternative, depending on teacher preference or student interest, you may prefer to fully cover some chapters and eliminate others. It is also possible to use Units 1 and 2 (Chapters 1–11) for a 90-day course and Units 3–5 (Chapters 12–23) as a second 90-day course. The teacher could then offer Food Science I and Food Science II for a full year of study.

TEACHING WITH FOOD SCIENCE

When planning the course, it is helpful to look over the suggested schedule for several chapters at a time. This will allow films to be ordered and guest speakers to be invited far enough in advance to be available when they are needed.

Students seem to be more motivated to learn chapter information when they carry out one of the experiments early in their study of the chapter. The first experiment can follow an initial introduction and presentation on chapter information. Following the experiment, additional activities, discussions, and the second experiment will continue the development of the material from the chapter. Students can then use "Check Your Facts" and "Critical Thinking and Problem Solving" to review the chapter content.

Before teaching a chapter, it is helpful to read the chapter, the background information in this *Guide*, and as much additional information as you need to feel comfortable with the material. It is best if you familiarize yourself with the experiments by carrying out each one before you have students conduct it. The experiment overview sections of this *Guide* provide "Helpful Hints" on how to prepare the materials used in the experiments as well as precautions you can take to ensure the success of the experiments.

As explained in Chapter 2, food science experimental samples are labeled with random three-digit numbers to prevent the number or letter of the sample from influencing the evaluation of the sample. While you may select your own three-digit sample numbers, this *Guide* gives suggested numbers for the experiments where random labeling of samples is important.

A suggested format for student laboratory reports is part of the text material in Chapter 1. The text suggests that students keep their laboratory reports in a notebook. If you prefer, **T-2: Laboratory Report Form** can be duplicated and used for students' reports. **T-3: Sample Laboratory Report** is a completed report, which can be duplicated and distributed to students to help them see how the reports should be pre-

pared. (Both also appear in the *Student Activity Workbook*.) If you do not choose to have students do complete reports, the data tables can be reproduced and used. It is generally helpful to allow some class time for students to work on their laboratory reports, since often data must be reported, exchanged, and analyzed.

In the overview of the experiments in this *Guide*, examples or descriptions of expected data are given. While students' data will vary, these examples will help you see whether the values obtained by your students are within normal expectations. If individual laboratory groups get results vastly different from the expected values, it is likely they did not follow the instructions, used incorrect quantities of materials, or misread their equipment (balance, thermometer, or graduated cylinder). If the entire class gets questionable results, check to be certain that the correct chemicals of the recommended concentrations were used and that the materials were fresh.

For several chapters, extension experiments or extensions of the experiments from the text are provided. The extension experiments are printed only in this *Teacher's Resource Guide*. These may be substituted for the regular experiments or carried out in addition to those in the textbook. Students who are more capable or are particularly interested in food science may carry out the extension activities as special projects.

If you have a class of lower-ability students, it is helpful to pronounce and discuss the "Terms to Remember" before asking students to read the chapter. This introduction to the vocabulary of the chapter will increase the students' understanding of chapter material as they read it.

It is probably also best to assign lower-ability students only the "Check Your Facts" questions at the end of each chapter. The answers to these questions can be found in the reading, while the answers to some of the other questions require more reasoning and problem solving by students.

The reproducible laboratory report form included in this *Guide* and the *Student Activity Workbook* is probably the easiest way to deal with laboratory reporting for lower-ability students. They will only need to fill in the blanks and answer the questions. As the experiments become more involved, you may want to demonstrate one of the two experiments included in the text for each chapter. The students can then conduct the other experiment. Another possibility is to limit the number of variables tested by the students during a given experiment. Every student would use the same variable or perhaps half of the class could do one of two variables tested. You can then use the expected data from this *Guide* to explain to students what would happen if other variables were tested.

Before the expected data in most of the experiments are two headings: Laboratory Simplification and Laboratory Enrichment. The laboratory simplifica-tion examples provide a guide to help you plan for students who may be having difficulty with the level of the lab work. The laboratory enrichment provides suggestions to help meet the needs of students who require more of a challenge.

In this *Teacher's Resource Guide*, the experiments labeled A and B will not be found in the *Student Activity Workbook*. They are provided to enable the teacher to have more experiments on certain topics, but also to provide a laboratory experiment that could be used as an authentic assessment. The students are tested on their ability to perform a laboratory experiment.

In an authentic assessment situation, it is important for the class and the teacher to design a rubric to show how the students' performance will be assessed. This would usually include such factors as laboratory organization, use of equipment, use of time, ability to follow directions, and interpretation of data.

EQUIPMENT AND SUPPLIES

Equipment

In the overview of the experiments in each chapter, equipment and supply lists are given. The following equipment list is a composite of those separate lists, and represents virtually all the equipment required for a food science classroom containing 12 laboratory stations intended for a class of 24 students. Traditional laboratory equipment is marked with an asterisk, and can be purchased from any scientific supply company.

Quantity Needed	Equipment Item
24	10-mL graduated cylinders, pyrex*
48	100-mL graduated cylinders, pyrex*
24	1000-mL beakers
24	150-mL beakers*
48	250-mL beakers*
48	250-mL Erlenmeyer flasks
48	400-mL beakers*
72	50-mL beakers*
24	600-mL beakers*
24	alcohol thermometers*, -20° – 100°C

Quantity Needed	Equipment Item
12	baking pans, square
6	balances, electronic
6	blenders or food processors
24	burets, glass*
12	cake pans, 23 cm diameter
6	can openers
12	454-mL canning jars
12	candy thermometers
12	coffee cans
12	corks, large*
12	custard cups or yogurt containers
12	cutting boards
12	electric mixers or hand beaters
1–2	food dehydrator(s)
12	forks
1	frying pan, aluminum
1	frying pan, aluminum w/non-stick coating
1	frying pan, cast iron

Quantity Needed	Equipment Item
1	frying pan, copper bottom, stainless steel
1	frying pan, porcelain enamel, cast iron
1	frying pan, stainless steel
1	frying pan, copper lined w/stainless steel
12	funnels*
24	glasses, small water
1	hot air popcorn popper
optional	incubators or yogurt makers
12	magnifying glasses*
12	measuring cups, 125 mL
12	measuring cups, 250 mL
12	measuring cups, 50 mL
12	medicine droppers*
24	metal diffusers (for electric stoves)
12	metric rulers*
12	microscope slides*
as many as possible up to 12	microscope(s)*
24	mixing bowls, large
4	muffin tins
12	needles, long
12	paring knives
12	pastry blenders
12	pie plates, clear
12	pins with plastic heads
5	pitchers, 1.0 L
24	plastic beakers*, set of
12	plastic or wooden spoons
12	plastic rings, 5.3 cm wide x 2.5 cm high
1	plastic squeeze bottle
24	ring stands with utility clamps*

Quantity Needed	Equipment Item
12	rolling pins
24	safety goggles
24	sauce pans
12	sauce pans, extra large
7	saucers or small plates
12	sifters
12	soup cans
12	spatulas, rubber
12	spatulas, straight edged
24	spoons, 5 mL
7	spoons, serving
12	stirring rods*
24	stoppers, one hole #0*
72	stoppers, solid #2*
12	strainers
12	test tube racks*
96	test tubes, pyrex, 18 x 150 mm*
12	tongs
15	trays, heat resistant
12	watch glasses*
12	wide mouth jars 0.9 L, with lids

The laboratory equipment required for each laboratory station is listed in this chart.

Quantity	Equipment
2	100-mL pyrex beakers
4	250-mL pyrex beakers
4	400-mL pyrex beakers
2	1000-mL pyrex beakers
2	set of plastic beakers
1	454-mL canning jar
4	250-mL Erlenmeyer flasks
2	10-mL pyrex graduated cylinders
4	100-mL pyrex graduated cylinders
2	alcohol thermometers -20° – 110°C
4	18 x 150-mm pyrex test tubes

Quantity	Equipment
2	test tube brushes
2	metal diffusers (for electric stoves)
2	glass burets
2	ring stands with utility clamps
2	one-hole stoppers
6	#2 stoppers
1	electronic balance

All of these items are standard laboratory equipment. They can be ordered from any scientific supply company. In some cases, it may be possible to borrow required items from the science department. It is not good practice to use old glassware for foods experiments where the products will be consumed, since some toxic chemicals may still be present on the glassware.

Many science departments are currently replacing their triple beam balances with digital electronic balances. There is a strong possibility that the science department in your school may have unneeded triple beam balances that they may be willing to give you. These can be safely used for food experiments because substances massed are placed on paper or in containers rather than directly on the balance pans. If purchasing balances, you should consider digital electronic balances for your classroom. Three should be ample.

Burets, which are expensive items only needed a couple of times during the year, may be borrowed if the chemistry teacher is willing to lend them to you. The borrowed equipment can be safely used because students do not ingest any of the chemicals used during the experiments requiring burets.

In addition to the laboratory equipment described above, each classroom should have an incubator, a food dehydrator, and a microscope. From time to time, students will also use normal food laboratory items such as wooden spoons, double boilers, candy thermometers, and saucepans.

It is worthwhile to check with the biology department about the possibility of borrowing one or more microscopes on the few occasions during the year when they are needed. This can be another way to limit the cost of introducing the course into the curriculum.

Supplies

The supplies required for food science for one class of students for one year range from traditional food items to a limited number of chemicals which must be purchased from a scientific supply company. The experiments in which each item is needed is listed, so that perishable items can be purchased as needed. The supply lists preceding each experiment indicate how much of each is required for one class for that particular lab. (Note that the dangerous materials have been rated according to the National Fire Protection Association's numerical identification system.)

Lab(s) Needed	Supply Item, Dangerous Material Rating	Amount
10-1	2,6 dichloroindophenol: H-2, F-1, R-1	0.5 g
17-1	agar prefilled Petri dishes	15 g or 12
2-1, 20-1	aluminum foil	2 rolls
14-1	angel food cake mix	2 boxes
2-1	anise extract	6 mL/ sm bottle
2-A	apple cubes	2 apples
10-1	apple juice, frozen	1 340-g can
12-1	apples	12
7-2	arrowroot	1 package
10-1	ascorbic acid: H-0, F-0, R-0	0.02 g
15-1	baker's yeast	24 g
14-1	baking powder—2 brands	1 can each
14-2	baking powder, double acting	1 can
3-1	beans	0.5 kg packages —3 kinds
8-1	beef, ground	1.2 kg
6-A	bleach, chlorine	200 mL
22-2	blindfolds	3–4
5-1, 5-A, 14-2	buttermilk	480 mL

Lab(s) Needed	Supply Item, Dangerous Material Rating	Amount
5-A	cabbage, red	1
10-2	calcium chloride: H-0, F-0, R-0	2 g
2-1	caraway seeds	6 mL
17-1	cellophane tape	1 roll
19-1	chicken broth	2.5 L
2-1	cinnamon	6 mL/ sm can
2-1	cloves	6 mL/ sm can
2-1	coffee, instant	6 mL/ sm can
22-2	cola	1.0 L each of 3 brands
7-1, 11-1	corn syrup	750 mL
5-1, 5-A	cranberry-apple juice	240 mL
5-1, 5-A, 7-1, 14-1, 14-2, 15-1	cream of tartar	167 g
13-A	cream, 18%	1.0 L
15-A	cucumbers	1 lug (flat)
13-A	cups, styrofoam—300–350 mL	12
2-2	dextrose	0.5 kg
21-2	dried fruit	24–48 pieces
5-1, 5-A, 9-1, 9-2, 9-3, 11-1, 13-2, 14-2	eggs	90
1-B, 4-A, 7-2, 8-2	flour, all-purpose	5.0 kg
14-2	flour, cake	1.3 kg
7-2	flour, rice	1 package
12-2	freezer bags	24
18-1	freezer bags, 0.5 L	12

Lab(s) Needed	Supply Item, Dangerous Material Rating	Amount
2-2	fructose	0.5 kg
12-2, 18-1	fruits and vegetables of choice	see labs
15-1	ginger	4.8 g
7-1	glycerol: H-1, F-1, R-0	10 mL
18-A	grapes, seedless	1.0 kg
7-1	half-and-half	0.5 L
5-1, 5-A	honey	240 mL
21-2	hydrogen peroxide	0.6 L
4-1	index cards	1 package
11-3	iodine, tincture of	1 small bottle
17-2	labels	48
2-2	lactose	0.5 kg
8-1, 8-2	lard	0.5 kg
2-1, 2-2, 5-1, 5-A, 12-1, 19-1, 21-1	lemon juice	3.5 L
5-1, 5-A	lemon-lime soda	240 mL
15-1	lime juice	12 mL
21-2	magnesium sulfate: H-0, F-0, R-0	30 g
2-2	maltose	0.5 kg
8-1, 8-2, 21-2	margarine	0.7 kg
2-A, 5-1, 7-1, 7-2, 8-1, 11-1, 12-1, 12-2, 14-2, 15-A, 16-2, 17-1, 18-1, 19-1, 19-2, 20-1, 20-2, 21-1	marking pen	3

Lab(s) Needed	Supply Item, Dangerous Material Rating	Amount
3-1, 7-1, 7-2, 11-1, 12-1, 12-2, 15-A, 16-2, 17-1, 17-2, 18-1, 19-1, 19-2, 20-1, 20-2, 21-1	masking tape	3 rolls
11-2	matches, wooden	1 box
17-2	methylene blue, 1:20,000, H-0, F-0, R-0	24 mL
5-1, 5-A, 10-2, 14-2, 17-2	milk	4.2 L
16-1	milk, 1%	1.9 L
16-1	milk, 2%	1.9 L
17-2	milk, fresh raw	1 L
16-1	milk, skim	1.9 L
17-2	milk, week old pasteurized	1 L
17-2	milk, week old raw	1 L
2-1, 5-1, 5-A	molasses	250 mL
2-1	mustard	6 mL
13-2	mustard, dry	1 can
22-2	non-cola	1.0 L
4-A	oil	1 bottle
2-1, 2-2	onion	2 onions
5-1, 5-A	orange drink, powdered	240 mL
20-2	orange juice, aseptically-canned	1.0 L
20-2	orange juice, freeze dried	1.0 L
20-2	orange juice, fresh squeezed	1.0 L
10-1, 20-2	orange juice, frozen	2 340-g cans
20-2	orange juice, pouch-canned	1.0 L
10-1	oxalic acid: H-3, F-0, R-0	12 g

Lab(s) Needed	Supply Item, Dangerous Material Rating	Amount
2-2, 16-2, 20-2, 22-2	paper cups, 32 mL	600
13-A	paper cups, wax coated, 75 mL	12
21-2	paper plates	12
16-2	paper plates, small	24
2-A, 18-2, 19-2	paper towels	2 rolls
11-2	peanuts	1 package
12-1	pears	12
19-2	peas, canned	1 can each of 6 different brands
2-1	peppermint extract	6 mL
5-1, 14-1, 14-2, 15-1, 15-A	pH paper 1–11 range	12 rolls
5-2	phenolphthalein: H-0, F-0, R-0	100 mL
15-A	plastic bags, 0.5 L	12
7-1, 12-1, 14-2, 20-1	plastic wrap	2 rolls
22-1	popping corn	1 unopened bag
1-A, 2-2	potassium chloride: H-0, F-0, R-0	150 g
6-1	potassium nitrate: H-1, F-0, R-0, Ox	0.1 kg
20-1	potato chips, flavored	1 package
20-1	potato chips, regular	1 package
2-A, 4-1, 4-2	potatoes	14
10-2	rennet	1.2 g
2-1	sauerkraut	6 mL
8-2, 14-2	shortening, hydrogenated	0.55 kg

Lab(s) Needed	Supply Item, Dangerous Material Rating	Amount
3-2, 5-1, 5-A, 14-1, 14-2	sodium bicarbonate: H-0, F-0, R-0	430 g
12-1, 18-1	sodium bisulfite: H-0, F-0, R-0	2.0 g
1-A, 2-2, 3-2, 6-1, 8-2, 11-1, 13-1, 13-2, 13-A, 14-2, 15-2, 15-A, 19-1, 19-2	sodium chloride: H-0, F-0, R-0	3.5 kg
10-2	sodium citrate: H-0, F-0, R-0	1.2 g
5-2	sodium hydroxide, 1.0 M: H-3, F-0, R-1	1.0 L
7-2, 21-1	souffle cups, baker's paper	2 boxes
2-1	soy sauce	6 mL
21-2	soybeans	1.7 kg
15-A	spices, assorted	see lab
7-2	starch, corn	1 package
7-2	starch, potato	1 package
2-2, 6-1, 7-1, 8-2, 9-1, 13-1, 14-2, 15-1, 15-2, 19-1, 21-1	sucrose	10.6 kg
1-B	sugar, brown	2000 mL
7-2	tapioca	1 package
2-1	tea leaves	6 mL
2-1	tobacco	6 mL
2-A	tofu	24 cc
4-1, 7-1	toothpicks, wooden	1 box
2-1, 13-A	vanilla extract	36 mL
21-1	vanilla pudding mixes (cooked)	12
8-2, 13-2	vegetable oil	3 L

Lab(s) Needed	Supply Item, Dangerous Material Rating	Amount
5-2	vinegar, cider	1.0 L
5-2	vinegar, rice	1.0 L
3-2, 5-1, 5-2, 5-A, 9-2, 11-1, 13-2, 14-2	vinegar, white	4.65 L
12-1	vitamin C tablets, 250 mg	8 tablets
11-2	walnuts	1 package
5-1, 21-2	water, deionized	1 L
6-A	water, pond	240 mL
14-2	waxed paper	1 roll
1-A	weighing paper	12 sheets
15-2	yeast, dry	48 g
16-2	yogurt	7 228-g containers, different flavors
16-1	yogurt, plain	0.5 L

In storing materials for food science, it is best to separate nonfood items from consumables to minimize the chance of someone mistakenly using a toxic substance in place of a consumable one. However, few further precautions are necessary since none of the chemicals needed are highly flammable or strong oxidizing agents.

The supply lists contain the materials needed for the experiments. Water is not included on the supply lists unless deionized or distilled water is required.

CHAPTER 1

What Is Food Science?

TEXT PAGES 14–33

SUGGESTED TIME SCHEDULE

180-day course—6 days.
90-day course—4 days.

STUDENT OBJECTIVES

- Define the study of food science and describe the main goal of food scientists.
- Explain the interrelationship of food science and nutrition.
- List the six main nutrients and food sources of each.
- Identify scientific equipment found in the laboratory and use it properly.
- Conduct food science experiments safely.
- Write accurate and complete reports on food science experiments.

CHAPTER SUMMARY

- Food science is the study of the production, processing, preparation, evaluation, and utilization of food.
- The major advances in food science have occurred over the last 200 years.
- Today food scientists work to improve the quality of food available.
- The six main nutrients needed for life and growth are water, carbohydrates, fat, protein, vitamins, and minerals.
- The Recommended Dietary Allowances (RDA) are levels of protein, vitamins, and minerals suggested for good health.
- The study of food science involves using equipment and supplies from both the foods and science laboratories.

- Using good safety habits is important in conducting successful food science experiments.
- An organized format for reporting laboratory results helps students learn the most from the experiments they perform.

BACKGROUND INFORMATION

Chapter 1 introduces students to the subjects of food science and nutrition and the interrelationship between these subjects. In addition, students learn about the laboratory equipment they will use and procedures for working safely in the laboratory.

It is important to explain the difference between food science and food preparation. The emphasis in food science is on why changes and reactions happen. For example, in food science, students study the physical and chemical changes that occur when an egg white is transformed from a clear liquid to a white solid. Food preparation students typically learn the procedures for frying or poaching the egg.

Food science is a very challenging field of study. No two foods are exactly alike; no two apples are identical because they receive different amounts of sunlight, water, and nutrients while they are growing. The complex nature of food has made it difficult to study. As a result, food science has traditionally been taught exclusively at the college level. It has only recently been introduced into the high school curriculum.

Teacher's Resource Guide
REPRODUCIBLE MATERIALS

T-1:   Laboratory Safety
T-2:   Food Science Laboratory Report Form

ACTIVITIES

1. Have students sample melon balls. Ask them to identify the chemicals in the melon. Distribute the pamphlet, "Your Breakfast Chemicals," available from: Consumer Information, Manufacturing Chemists Association, 1825 Connecticut Ave. N.W., Washington, D.C. 20009. Discuss with students the "natural" chemicals found in food.

2. Talk with students about the history of food science and nutrition and the new advances being made in research in these fields. Newspapers and magazines frequently cover the most recent developments in the field and should be good resources for generating enthusiasm in students for the up-to-date nature of the study of food science.

3. Ask students to locate articles related to food science or nutrition in newspapers or magazines and bring copies of the articles to class. Have students give brief oral reports summarizing the content of these articles.

4. Invite a food scientist to class to discuss careers in food science, what a food scientist does, and the education needed for a career in food science.

5. Explain the differences and similarities between the Recommended Dietary Allowances (RDA) and the United States Recommended Daily Allowances (U.S. RDA). Have students each bring a food label to class that lists the U.S. RDA for nutrients in the product. Where possible, compare the U.S. RDA figures with those on the RDA charts. In what categories do the amounts differ? What causes the differences?

6. Invite a nutritionist or dietitian to class to discuss the relationship of nutrition and health. Other topics could include healthy eating patterns and dietary planning.

7. Display and name common laboratory equipment. Demonstrate the proper use of the equipment, including the assembly of a ring stand, iron ring, and clamps. Show students how thermometers and burets can be supported by the ring stand assembly during experiments.

8. Discuss with students the use of the metric system of measurement in food science. *Food Science* uses only metric measures unless customary measures are needed for the use of equipment such as the oven or a candy thermometer. Students need to be comfortable with the concept of mass instead of weight and the use of the Celsius temperature scale.

9. Divide students into small groups. Have the groups brainstorm to develop a list of safety practices for laboratory work. Have one student from each group report so the class can develop a master list of safe laboratory practices. Stress the importance of safe rules and procedures in working in the laboratory. Use **T-1: Laboratory Safety**, which is printed in the *Guide* and in the *Student Activity Workbook*, to reinforce the importance of laboratory safety.

10. Discuss with students the reporting format for experiments. Use **T-3: Sample Laboratory Report** as an example of how a laboratory report should be prepared. If desired, use **T-2: Laboratory Report Form** for students' use in writing laboratory reports. Both are printed in the *Guide* and in the *Student Activity Workbook*.

11. In preparation for **Experiment 1-1: Using an Electronic Balance**, demonstrate the use of the triple beam balance. Mass an object, a sample of sugar or salt on weighing paper, and a liquid.

12. In preparation for **Experiment 1-2: Using a Graduated Cylinder**, demonstrate how to read the volume of liquid in a graduated cylinder.

13. If **Experiment 1-B: Precision in Measurement** is not conducted by students, follow the experiment procedure to demonstrate the greater accuracy of mass measurements as compared to volume measurements.

EXTENSION ACTIVITY

Have students conduct **Experiment 1-B: Precision in Measurement**.

OVERVIEW OF EXPERIMENTS

- ### *Experiment 1-1:* USING AN ELECTRONIC BALANCE

Time Required

20 minutes

Objective

Students will learn to use an electronic balance.

Equipment

- 3 electronic balances
- 3 items to be massed on each balance—suggested items to mass include: paper clips, scissors, beakers, or cooking utensils. Ideally, one item should have a mass of less than 10 g, one item should have a mass between 10–100 g, and one item should have a mass greater than 100 g.

Supplies

- 3 containers table salt
- weighing paper
- 3 5-mL spoons
- 3 straight-edged spatulas

Helpful Hints

- Be sure to remind students that electronic balances are expensive and must be treated with care. Demonstrate how to use the balances students will use in the classroom before they begin the experiment. Explain how to read the scales.
- At no time should students press the function button since this will cause the balance to give readings in units other than grams.
- Solids should be massed on weighing or waxed paper or in a container; liquids must be massed in a container.
- Demonstrate the use of the tare button to cancel the mass of the weighing paper or container.
- Point out that chemicals should never be placed directly on the balance pan.

Laboratory Simplification

None.

Laboratory Enrichment

During this experiment or **Experiment 1-A: Using a Triple Beam Balance**, have students determine the mass of a given quantity of water, using a small graduated cylinder as the container. Also, have students mass a specified amount of a dry chemical, such as 25 g table salt or sugar.

Expected Data

Results will vary depending on items massed. The mass of 5 mL of table salt is about 6.5 g.

● Experiment 1-2: USING A GRADUATED CYLINDER

Time Required

20 minutes

Objective

Students will learn to use the meniscus to read the volume of liquids.

Equipment

- 12 100-mL graduated cylinders
- 12 100-mL beakers

Supplies

- none

Helpful Hints

- Demonstrate for students how to read the volume of a liquid in a narrow container using the bottom of the curve, or meniscus, formed by the liquid. There are a few liquids with very high surface tension, such as mercury, that form an upward meniscus. In these cases, the top of the curve is used to read the volume. However, students will not need to take volume readings of any of these liquids in this course.
- For the greatest accuracy, the cylinder should be placed on a level surface and be read at eye level.

Laboratory Simplification

None.

Laboratory Enrichment

Have students transfer exactly 20.0 mL from a buret to a grade cylinder. Read volume in grade cylinder.

Expected Data

Beaker Reading	Graduated Cylinder Reading
20 mL	18 mL
30 mL	26 mL
25 mL	23 mL

• Experiment 1-A: USING A TRIPLE BEAM BALANCE

Note: The procedure for this experiment is printed only in the *Teacher's Resource Guide*. This experiment is an alternative to **Experiment 1-1: Using an Electronic Balance**.

Time Required

20 minutes

Objective

Students will learn to use a triple beam balance.

Equipment

- 6 triple beam balances
- 3 items to be massed on each balance

Supplies

- none

Helpful Hints

- Be sure to demonstrate how to use the balances students will use in the classroom before they begin the experiment. Explain how to read the scales.
- Liquids must be massed in a previously massed container, while solid chemicals must be massed on previously massed weighing paper or waxed paper.
- Remind students that chemicals must never be placed directly on the balance pan.
- Remind students that if the balance does not zero properly, they should call you to adjust it, rather than attempting to do so themselves.

Laboratory Simplification

None.

Laboratory Enrichment

1. During **Experiment 1-1: Using an Electronic Balance**, have students mass a dry chemical, such as table salt or sugar, to gain practice using weighing paper.
2. During **Experiment 1-1: Using an Electronic Balance** or during this experiment, have students determine the mass of a given quantity of water, using a small graduated cylinder as the container. Also, have students mass a specified amount of a dry chemical, such as 25 g table salt or sugar.

Expected Data

Results will vary, depending on the items massed.

• Experiment 1-B: PRECISION IN MEASUREMENT

Note: The procedure for this experiment is printed only in the *Teacher's Resource Guide*.

Time Required

45 minutes

Objective

Students will learn that using mass is a more accurate way of measuring materials because it eliminates the variations caused by the air spaces that occur between particles of solids.

Equipment

- 6 triple beam balances/3 electronic balances
- 12 250-mL measuring cups
- 12 125-mL measuring cups
- 12 50-mL measuring cups
- 12 straight-edged spatulas
- 6 sifters
- 12 spoons

Supplies

- 2000 mL all-purpose flour
- 2000 mL brown sugar

Helpful Hints

- When the readings are averaged in this experiment, the values for 5 times the 50-mL cup measurements and 2 times the 125-mL cup measurements will be quite close to the averages for the 250-mL cup measurements. However, readings for individual laboratory groups will generally produce inconsistent results when the values from the smaller measures are multiplied to determine the value for the 250-mL cup.

Laboratory Simplification

Measure only 250-mL measuring cups.

Laboratory Enrichment

None.

Expected Data

Results will vary.

ANSWER KEY

Student Text

● ANSWERS TO QUESTIONS IN TEXT:

p. 17   2000 g.

p. 21

1. Water and carbohydrates.
2. A three-year-old would need small portions of foods high in vitamins, minerals and proteins, while an elderly person should probably eat a salad, or fruits and nonfat yogurt—foods lower in fats, sugar, and protein.

p. 24

Use a graduated cylinder to measure known volumes of water, for example, 10 mL portions. Pour these into the beaker and mark the beaker at the 10, 20, 30 mL, etc. amounts and then use it for measuring other samples of liquid.

p. 25   21°C.

p. 26

No, the combined mass of the sugar and beaker would exceed the limit of the balance.

p. 30

The information should appear in your observations.

● CHECK YOUR FACTS

1. The study of the production, processing, preparation, evaluation, and utilization of food.
2. The development of effective methods for detecting harmful substances in food and new laws regarding food safety.
3. Water, carbohydrates, fat, protein, vitamins, and minerals.
4. 5 years. They are revised when new research shows more or less of a nutrient is needed for good health.
5. For measuring volume.
6. An Erlenmeyer flask.
7. To prevent the balance pan from corroding.
8. So the student will know what to do when conducting the experiment.
9. If all the liquid has boiled away, the beaker will break.
10. Return equipment to its proper place; turn off stove elements and oven; clean countertops, sink, and stove; wash your hands; place towels and dishcloths in designated place.
11. Liquids or water-soluble materials.

● CRITICAL THINKING AND PROBLEM SOLVING

1. Food science is concerned with the production, processing, preparation, evaluation, and utilization of food while nutrition is concerned with understanding how food is used by the body. Food scientists work to provide food that has the highest nutritional value to as many people as possible.
2. Most people will get enough carbohydrates and fat if they meet the RDA for other nutrients.
3. Both are recommendations based on research that are used to help people meet their bodies' nutritional needs. The RDA are more specific and are based on age, sex, pregnancy, and lactation. The U.S. RDA are averages and are not as precise.
4. Read the volume from the bottom of the meniscus.
5. There will be no way to know exactly how much liquid is in the cylinder.
6. If the liquid is to be swirled, use an Erlenmeyer flask, otherwise use the beaker.
7. Transfer the liquid to a smaller container so the liquid would be deep enough to cover the thermometer bulb.
8. Massing is done on a balance while weighing is done on a scale. Mass is a measure of the amount

of matter in a sample while weight is the gravitational attraction between an object and the earth. Mass is constant while weight changes as the distance between the object and the center of the earth changes.

9. First mass a piece of weighing paper, then set the balance to a reading 10 g heavier than the mass of the paper. Add salt until the pointer comes to rest on the zero line.

10. The riders on the beam are set at a value that is heavier than the mass of the material on the pan.

Student Activity Workbook

● H-1-1: STUDY GUIDE

1. chemicals
2. Food science
3. the late 1700s
4. harmful substances
5. Nutrition
6. nutrient
7. water
8. sugar
9. fat
10. protein
11. Vitamins
12. minerals
13. Recommended Dietary Allowances (RDA)
14. eating habits
15. beaker
16. volume
17. meniscus
18. buret
19. Petri dish
20. Celsius
21. mass
22. Weight
23. equipment
24. closed
25. wash them immediately
26. a cutting board
27. metal trivet
28. Insoluble
29. procedure
30. conclusion

● H-1-2: SCRAMBLED WORDS

1. Erlenmeyer flask
2. insoluble
3. thermometer
4. data
5. meniscus
6. graduated cylinder
7. trivet
8. beaker
9. balance
10. calibrate
11. buret
12. food science

● H-1-3: ANALOGIES

1. c
2. d
3. a
4. b
5. c
6. a
7. b
8. c
9. a
10. d

● H-1-4: FOOD SCIENCE EQUIPMENT

1. beaker
2. graduated cylinder
3. test tube
4. filter funnel
5. ring stand and ring
6. clamp
7. Erlenmeyer flask
8. test tube clamp
9. test tubes and rack

● H-1-5: NUTRITION AND YOU

1. Athletes particularly need water and carbohydrates.
2. Women require more calcium and iron.
3. Infants and small children require the most nutrients.
4. Older individuals should eat more fruits and vegetables, since these foods are low in fat and sugar.
5. Eating properly allows athletes to develop greater endurance, lose excess body weight, and strengthen muscles.
6. Athletes should eat food high in carbohydrate because it provides the energy needed to perform well.
7. Perspiring helps to prevent body temperature from rising during strenuous activity.
8. Adolescents and pregnant women require the largest quantities of nutrients.
9. Answers will vary.
10. Answers will vary, but values at age 40 will be less than the student's nutritional needs now.

● T-1: LABORATORY SAFETY

1. Wash hands
2. safety goggles
3. understand
4. Do not
5. cutting board
6. metal trivet
7. hot glass
8. Turn off
9. empty
10. report

● Experiment 1-1: USING AN ELECTRONIC BALANCE

1. 1 g—the mass of a penny is approximately 3.2 g.
2. Mass an empty 10-mL graduated cylinder, add exactly 10 mL water, and mass again. The mass of the water is the difference in mass between the two readings.

Experiment 1-2: USING A GRADUATED CYLINDER

1. Not very precise.
2. The graduated cylinder.
3. Each cylinder is calibrated individually while the same care is not taken in putting the lines on beakers.

Teacher's Resource Guide

• Experiment 1-A: USING A TRIPLE BEAM BALANCE

1. 1 g—the mass of a penny is approximately 3.2 g.
2. Mass an empty 10-mL graduated cylinder, add exactly 10 mL water, and mass again. The mass of the water is the difference in mass between the two readings.

• Experiment 1-B: PRECISION IN MEASUREMENT

1. The sifted flour.
2. The sifted flour; the packed brown sugar.

• LABORATORY SAFETY QUIZ

1. sink
2. open
3. closed
4. T
5. plugs
6. T

7. X
8.
9. X
10. X
11. X
12. X
13. A. Answers will vary with classroom.
    B. Answers will vary with classroom.
    C. Answers will vary with classroom.
14. d.
15. a.
16. c.
17. c.
18. b.
19. b.
20. d.
21. d.
22. c.
23. d.
24. c.
25. g.
26. a.
27. j.
28. i.
29. h.
30. c.
31. e.
32. b.
33. f.
34. d.
35. A. Flush with water from eye wash bottles/eye wash station. Immediately notify teacher.
    B. Wear safety goggles in laboratory when heating caustic substances.
36. A. Use fire blanket. Stop, drop, roll, and smother fire.
    B. Always remove, or tie back, and roll up loose clothing and sleeves.
37. A. Ventilate area. Alert teacher. Step back.
    B. Never combine unmarked samples. Always mark containers immediately as items come from marked chemical bottles.

Chapter 1: What Is Food Science?

LABORATORY SAFETY

TEXT PAGES 14-33

DIRECTIONS: Fill in the blanks in each sentence below.

1. _____ prior to all laboratory work.

2. Wear aprons and _____ as needed.

3. Read and _____ directions before beginning laboratory work.

4. _____ lick your fingers.

5. Do all cutting on a _____ .

6. Always use a _____ or insulating pad when heating beakers on the stove.

7. Remember—_____ looks like cold glass!

8. _____ stove elements when finished using them.

9. Never heat an _____ beaker—remove the beaker from the stove before its contents boil away.

10. Clean up all broken glass and _____ breakage to your teacher.

FOOD SCIENCE LABORATORY REPORT FORM

LABORATORY PREPARATION: Complete this section of the report before conducting the experiment.

Number and Title of Experiment: _____

Performed by:_____ Class Period:_____

Partner: _____ Date:_____

Purpose of Experiment:

Experiment Procedure:

LABORATORY RESULTS: Complete this section of the report during and after the experiment.

Observations:

Data: Attach completed data table to this report.

Calculations:

Questions:

Conclusion:

FOOD SCIENCE LABORATORY REPORT FORM
Sample Laboratory Report

LABORATORY PREPARATION: Complete this section of the report before conducting the experiment.

Number and Title of Experiment: _I-A: Using a Triple Beam Balance_

Performed by: _Jane Doe_ (your name) _____ Class Period: _4_

Partner: _Jim Dean_ (your partner's name) Date: _September 6_

Purpose of Experiment: _to become familiar with the triple beam balance._

Experiment Procedure: _Check the balance for accuracy when the pan is empty. Place objects on the pan and adjust weights. Read the mass indicated. Record the mass of the object in the data table._

LABORATORY RESULTS: Complete this section of the report during and after the experiment.

Observations: _The mass of the scissors was the greatest. The triple beam balance was hard to adjust._

Data:

Object	Mass
Paper clip	5.0g
Beaker	126.8g
Scissors	196.9g

Calculations: _This example is using weighing paper._
Mass of weighing paper – 4g.
Mass of paper and paper clip – 9g.
Subtract mass of weighing paper from total mass.
9g – 4g = 5g = mass of paper clip.

Questions: _1. The mass of a penny would be closer to 1g._
2. Mass an empty 10mL graduated cylinder, add exactly 10mL water, and mass again. The mass of the water is the difference between the two readings.

Conclusion: _When accuracy is important in measuring mass, the triple beam balance should be used. The triple beam balance can be time-consuming to use, but it is very accurate._

EXPERIMENT 1-A
Using a Triple Beam Balance

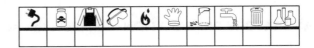

You are going to have many opportunities to mass substances in food science. Therefore one of the first skills you need to learn is how to use a balance, the instrument you will use to mass materials. This experiment is designed to teach you to use a laboratory balance.

At each laboratory station you will find either a low-form or a high-form triple beam balance. Either form is simply called a balance. If the balance does not zero properly, ask your teacher to correct the problem.

PROCEDURE

1. Obtain three objects to be massed from your teacher.
2. Place one object on the balance pan with all the riders set on zero. This will cause the pointer to point to the top of the scale.
3. Move the 100–g rider out to the first notch on its beam. If the pointer drops all the way to the bottom of the scale, 100 g is too much. You would then return this rider to zero. If the pointer does not drop, move the rider to the 200–g mark. Again, if this is too heavy, move it back to 100 g.
4. Next move the 10–g rider along its beam, one notch at a time, until the pointer drops to the bottom of the scale. When this happens, move the rider back to the previous notch.
5. Now slide the 1–g rider along its arm until the pointer settles exactly at zero.

6. You are ready to read the balance. The mass of the object on the balance is the sum of the values of the three riders. Assume the riders on your balance are arranged as follows—the first is on the 100–g notch, the second is on the 60–g notch, and the last is at what you estimate to be 2.65 g (meaning it is halfway between 2.6–2.7). The mass of the object is 162.65 grams.
7. In a data table similar to the sample data table shown below, record the name of the object and its mass.
8. Mass each of the other objects and record the information in your data table.

QUESTIONS

1. Do you think a penny would have a mass closer to 1 g, 10 g, or 100 g?
2. If you had to determine the mass of 10 mL water, how would you do it?

SAMPLE DATA TABLE

Object	Mass

EXPERIMENT 1-B
Precision in Measurement

In all areas of science, it is important to measure quantities of materials as precisely as possible. In this experiment, you will compare the masses of designated volumes of solids to determine whether measuring by mass or by volume gives more precise results.

PROCEDURE

1. Mass 250–mL, 125–mL, and 50–mL empty measuring cups. Record the masses in your data table.
2. Follow the variation assigned by your teacher.
   a. **Variation 1**. Lightly spoon all-purpose flour into the 250–mL measuring cup. Level the flour with the straight edge of a metal spatula. Mass the flour and cup. Using the same flour, spoon the flour into the 125–mL cup, level, and mass. Spoon flour into the 50–mL cup, level, and mass. Record these values in your data table.
   b. **Variation 2**. Sift all-purpose flour. Lightly spoon the sifted flour into the 250–mL measuring cup. Level the flour with the straight edge of a metal spatula. Mass the flour and cup. Resift the massed flour. Fill the 125–mL cup with the resifted flour, level, and mass. Fill the 50–mL cup, level, and mass. Record these values in your data table.
   c. **Variation 3**. Lightly spoon brown sugar into the 250–mL measuring cup. Level the cup with the straight edge of a metal spatula. Mass the brown sugar and cup. Using the same sugar, lightly spoon brown sugar into the 125–mL cup, level, and mass. Lightly spoon brown sugar into the 50–mL cup, level, and mass. Record these values in your data table.
   d. **Variation 4**. Firmly press brown sugar into the 250–mL measuring cup. Level the cup with the straight edge of a metal spatula. Mass the brown sugar and cup. Using the

same sugar, firmly press brown sugar into the 125–mL cup, level, and mass. Firmly press brown sugar into the 50–mL cup, level, and mass. Record these values in your data table.

3. Determine the mass of each solid by subtracting the mass of the empty measuring cup from the mass of the cup and solid. Record the mass of your solid in your data table and on the chalkboard.
4. Average the results written on the chalkboard for each solid. Record the averaged values in your data table.

QUESTIONS

1. Multiply the average mass of each 50 mL measurement by 5 and each 125 mL measurement by 2. For which substance are these values closest to the mass of 250 mL as measured on the balance?
2. Which gave more precise results, the sifted or unsifted flour? The firmly pressed or lightly spooned brown sugar?

SAMPLE DATA TABLE

Mass	250-mL Cup	125-mL Cup	50-mL Cup
Empty Cup			
Cup and flour or sugar			
Flour or sugar			
Average of Variation 1			
Average of Variation 2			
Average of Variation 3			
Average of Variation 4			

LABORATORY SAFETY QUIZ

DIRECTIONS: Correct the underlined words of each false statement to make the statement true. Write the correct word that should be placed in the sentence in the blank space on the left. True statements will not need correction. Mark them with a T.

_____ 1. When working with acids and bases, pour them from one container to another over your <u>work bench</u> in the laboratory.

_____ 2. Always heat liquids in a container that is <u>closed</u>.

_____ 3. Keep the lids of all chemical containers <u>open</u> when not in use.

_____ 4. Use a <u>twisting</u> motion to insert a glass thermometer into a rubber stopper.

_____ 5. Grasp appliance <u>cords</u> firmly and pull gently when removing from an electrical outlet.

_____ 6. Place a <u>wire gauze</u> between the glass and the flame when heating flasks and beakers.

DIRECTIONS: Place an X by those rules that should be observed when handling sharp utensils such as knives.

_____ 7. Do not grab for them when they are falling.

_____ 8. Carry with tip pointing toward you.

_____ 9. Do not talk with them in your hands.

_____ 10. Use only for purpose or job intended.

_____ 11. Store where easily seen.

_____ 12. Do not handle when hands are slippery or greasy.

DIRECTIONS: Tell where each of the following is located in your food science laboratory.

13a. Eye Wash Station:_____

_____

_____

13b. Fire Extinguisher: _____

_____

_____

13c. Fire Blanket: _____

_____

_____

DIRECTIONS: Write the letter of the correct answer on the line to the left of the item number.

_____ 14. If your hand is splashed with sodium hydroxide, you should
a. dry your hand quickly.
b. place hand under a faucet of running water.
c. notify your teacher right away.
d. b and c.

_____ 15. When glass is broken, you should
a. notify your teacher immediately.
b. quickly pick up the glass.
c. sweep the floor immediately.
d. place glass in trash can.

_____ 16. If you find a bottle of a chemical at your lab station that is unlabeled, you should
a. taste the unbottled chemical to attempt to identify it.
b. throw the bottle in the trash.
c. give the bottle to the teacher.
d. look inside the bottle to identify the chemical by sight.

_____ 17. When stirring a solution, you should use
a. a metal spoon.
b. a pencil.
c. a glass stirring rod.
d. All of the above.

_____ 18. Treat any and all microorganisms as if they were
a. safe.
b. harmful.
c. alive.
d. sterile.

_____ 19. You may eat or drink in a food science laboratory
a. never.
b. when specific lab activities require tasting.
c. only after you wash your hands.
d. anytime you want.

_____ 20. When working in the food science laboratory,
a. wear goggles when eye caution is required.
b. tie back long hair and loose clothing.
c. wear a protective apron.
d. All of the above.

_____ 21. It is important to
a. unplug electrical equipment after use.
b. place broken glass in a special container.
c. keep work area organized and uncluttered.
d. All of the above.

_____ 22. To safely move a beaker of hot liquid
a. use a hot pad.
b. use two test-tube holders.
c. use the large beaker tongs.
d. any of the above.

_____ 23. When filling a buret,
a. always pour away from you.
b. stand above the buret to protect your eyes.
c. always use a pipet to fill it.
d. always wear goggles.

_____ 24. All chemicals should be disposed by
a. flushing down the sink with hot water.
b. flushing down the sink with cold water.
c. specific directions provided by your teacher.
d. placing them in the garbage can.

DIRECTIONS: The safety symbols used for the labs are illustrated in the left-hand column. The messages for each symbol are on the right. In the blank before each symbol, write the letter for the message of that symbol.

_____ 25.

_____ 26.

_____ 27.

_____ 28.

_____ 29.

_____ 30.

_____ 31.

_____ 32.

_____ 33.

_____ 34.

a. Take care to avoid injury to hands.

b. Chemicals may produce hazards.

c. Be careful when using electrical equipment.

d. Wear appropriate laboratory clothing.

e. Eye protection is required.

f. Potential fire hazards exist.

g. Be attentive to specific instructions for use of equipment.

h. Sound personal hygiene habits should be observed.

i. The danger of breaking glassware exists.

j. Dispose of products as directed.

DIRECTIONS: Below, tell (A) how to deal with emergency and (B) how each could have been prevented.

35. A caustic substance splashes out of a test tube into the eye of your lab partner while he is heating the substance.

A. _____

_____

B. _____

_____

36. The loose, puffy sleeve of a classmate catches fire as she reaches across the gas burner of the stove.

A. _____

_____

B. _____

_____

37. Your lab group combines two chemicals improperly from unmarked test tubes.

A. _____

_____

B. _____

_____

The Scientific Evaluation of Food

TEXT PAGES 34–47

SUGGESTED TIME SCHEDULE

180-day course—8 days.
90-day course—4 days.

STUDENT OBJECTIVES

- Define sensory evaluation.
- Identify the qualities that make up the sensory characteristics of food.
- List qualifications needed for a career in sensory evaluation.
- Explain what sensory evaluation panels do and how they are conducted.
- Describe characteristics of successful sensory testing.
- Discuss factors affecting people's food preferences.

CHAPTER SUMMARY

- Sensory evaluation involves scientifically testing the quality of food using the human senses of sight, smell, taste, touch, and hearing.
- The sensory characteristics of food are appearance, odor, flavor, mouthfeel, and sound.
- Sensory evaluation can be an exciting and satisfying career for a person interested in science and food.
- Sensory evaluation panels help evaluate new and existing food products and can be composed of trained experts or consumers.
- Conditions for successful sensory testing must be highly controlled.
- In addition to the sensory qualities of food, people's food likes and dislikes may be affected by cultural heritage, level of hunger, and advertising.

BACKGROUND INFORMATION

Chapter 2 introduces students to the scientific evaluation of food. Qualities of food tested during sensory evaluation, terminology, and techniques used in determining which foods appeal to individuals are discussed.

Students will be interested to learn that sensory evaluators of major food companies earn, on the average, higher salaries than many engineers and architects. One reason is that, so far, no machine can evaluate flavor because doing so is such a complex task.

Americans tend to prefer immediate flavors. They don't like to have to chew for long periods of time to develop flavor. Internationally, orange is the most popular flavor.

Children tend to adopt the food preferences of their parents simply because they are exposed to the foods their parents serve them. Humans can learn to like virtually any food. This is one reason people have been able to survive in so many climates.

Teacher's Resource Guide
REPRODUCIBLE MATERIALS

T-4:   What Is Sensory Evaluation?
E-2-A: Mouthfeel and Sensory Evaluation

ACTIVITIES

1. Have students sample foods with a wide variety of sensory qualities. If possible, include some foods with which students may not be familiar.

Discuss with students the characteristics that influence whether they like or dislike a particular food.

2. Discuss with students the components of sensory evaluation (appearance, odor, flavor, mouthfeel, and sound) and why sensory evaluation is a scientific approach to evaluating food. Use **T-4: What Is Sensory Evaluation?** to reinforce the link between human senses and the components of sensory evaluation. It is printed in the *Guide* and in the *Student Activity Workbook*.

3. Invite a sensory evaluator to speak to the class on careers in sensory evaluation, what a sensory evaluator does, and the education and training needed for a career in sensory evaluation.

4. Have students read the following article: "Autumn Leaves," *Chem Matters*, October 1986, page 7. Use the article as the basis of a discussion on the role color plays in the appearance of food.

5. Have students read one or both of the following articles: "The Intimate Sense of Smell," *National Geographic*, September 1986, Page 324, or "Chemists Whip up a Tasty Mess of Artificial Flavors," *Smithsonian*, May 1986, page 79. Discuss the article(s) with students, highlighting the role of smell in sensory evaluation.

6. Discuss the various aspects of mouthfeel such as temperature, shape and form, spiciness, consistency, chewiness, astringency (sourness), graininess, brittleness, and thickness (viscosity). Have students identify foods whose mouthfeel is characterized by the qualities listed above.

7. Show the film: "The Sugar Film," IMAS, 1980 (28 minutes).

8. Introduce students to the concept of cultural characteristics of food and why certain food combinations survived in some areas. If appropriate, have students discuss their own food heritages.

9. Invite a person from a foreign country to talk about ethnic foods, eating patterns, and food preparation in the person's native land.

10. In preparation for **Experiment 2-2: Flavor Comparison**, explain how to prepare mass percent solutions and have students prepare the solutions for the experiment.

EXTENSION ACTIVITY

Have students conduct **Experiment 2-A: Mouthfeel and Sensory Evaluation**.

OVERVIEW OF EXPERIMENTS

● *Experiment 2-1:* ODOR RECOGNITION

Time Required

45 minutes

Objective

Students will discover how difficult it is to identify common foods by odor alone and will recognize how interdependent the senses are in food evaluation.

Equipment

- 45 test tubes
- 3 test tube racks

Supplies

- cloves
- cinnamon
- soy sauce
- instant coffee
- tea leaves
- caraway seeds
- sauerkraut
- lemon juice
- molasses
- peppermint extract
- tobacco
- vanilla extract
- anise extract
- onion
- mustard
- aluminum foil

Helpful Hints

- For a class of 24 students, prepare three sets of test tubes in test tube racks. Have four laboratory groups work with each set of test tubes.
- To eliminate the sense of sight, wrap the tubes in aluminum foil and cover them with pieces of foil or cork stoppers. Rubber stoppers have too strong an odor of their own and will mask the odors of the substances in the tubes.
- Place about 1 mL of each substance in a test tube. Label each test tube with a three-digit number. Gum labels work well. Be sure to cover the test tubes after filling them. Store the test tubes in the

refrigerator if you prepare them more than one day in advance.

- Take the test tubes out of the refrigerator two hours before the experiment is to be preformed so the substances can warm enough to produce sufficient odor to be detected.
- Students should work in their usual laboratory groups with one partner blindfolded as the other partner uncovers one sample at a time and holds the test tube under the partner's nose. The partners not wearing the blindfolds should not look into the test tubes since this would give them an unfair advantage when it is their turn to guess the contents of the test tubes. The partner holding the sample records (in the partner's data table) the number of the test tube and the partner's guess of what is in the tube. Once all 15 test tubes have been sniffed, the partners reverse roles and repeat the procedure.
- Stress to students that it is important to work quietly so that one student's answers do not influence others. Try to keep conditions as uniform as possible for all students.
- At the end of the experiment, tell students the identity of the substances.

Laboratory Simplification

Select ten samples only.

Laboratory Enrichment

Students select three samples found at home and perform the experiment with family members.

Expected Data

Answers will vary drastically, depending on how skilled students are at identifying colors.

Code	Blindfolded Identification	Actual Identity of Substance
693		cloves
931		cinnamon
542		soy sauce
112		instant coffee
127		tea leaves
213		caraway seeds
719		sauerkraut
443		lemon juice
357		molasses
857		peppermint extract
319		tobacco
115		vanilla extract
276		anise extract
601		onion
573		mustard

● Experiment 2-2: FLAVOR COMPARISON

Time Required

30 minutes

Objective

Students will determine the degree of sweetness, sourness, and saltiness of various solutions to gain further experience in sensory evaluation.

Equipment

- 15 1000-mL beakers or pitchers
- 15 trays

Supplies

- 360 32 mL paper cups
- 0.5 kg fructose**
- 0.5 kg dextrose**
- 0.5 kg lactose**
- 0.5 kg sucrose**
- 0.5 kg maltose**
- 1.9 L lemon juice
- 0.9 kg sodium chloride
- 150 g potassium chloride

**Make sure you get purified substances that can be consumed by humans.*

Helpful Hints

- Fructose and sucrose are available at most grocery stores. Dextrose, lactose, and maltose are available at health food stores.
- Prepare 1000 mL of each solution at the concentrations listed below. To prepare 20 percent solutions, add 200 g solid to 800 mL (g) water. To prepare 15 percent solutions, add 150 g solid to 850 mL water etc. To prepare the lemon juice solutions, add 100 mL lemon juice to 900 mL water for the 10 percent solution, 150 mL lemon juice to 850 mL water for the 15 percent solution, etc. All solutions should be at room temperature.

Sugar solutions:	813	fructose	20%
	241	sucrose	20%
	552	maltose	20%
	763	dextrose	20%
	184	lactose	20%
Sour solutions:	413	lemon juice	10%
	264	lemon juice	15%
	156	lemon juice	20%
	925	lemon juice	25%
	378	lemon juice	30%
Alternate	378	pure water	
Salt solutions:	189	sodium chloride	5%
	566	sodium chloride	15%
	489	sodium chloride	25%
	235	potassium chloride	15%
	631	pure water	

- This experiment can be organized by having three tasting sites—sweet, sour, and salty. The class can be divided into three groups which rotate from one testing site to the next.

- Place a beaker of solution labeled with a three-digit number (such as those above) on a tray. On the same tray, place 24 cups labeled with the same three-digit number as the beaker. Each tasting site will have five trays.
- Have each student pour a small amount of each solution into a cup for testing.
- Vinegar can be used for the sour substance instead of lemon juice.
- Have students write their data on a table on the chalkboard. They will need this information to answer the experiment questions.
- Discuss how similar (or different) class results were. Also discuss how close the class results were to the table values for sweetness.

Laboratory Simplification

Do only sweet and sour samples.

Laboratory Enrichment

None.

Expected Data

The order of sweetness of sugar solutions as identified in research is (from most sweet to least sweet): fructose, sucrose, dextrose, maltose, and lactose.

Generally, the salt solutions should be in order of concentration. However, potassium chloride seems saltier or stronger than sodium chloride and so is usually listed higher than it would be based on concentration.

The sour solutions are in order of concentration.

● Experiment 2-A: MOUTHFEEL AND SENSORY EVALUATION

Note: The procedure for this experiment is printed only in the *Teacher's Resource Guide*.

Time Required

30 minutes

Objective

Students will distinguish between food samples on the basis of mouthfeel alone by tasting samples similar in appearance and holding their noses to eliminate the sense of smell.

Equipment

- 4 trays

Supplies

- 24 1-cm apple cubes
- 24 1-cm onion cubes
- 24 1-cm potato cubes
- 24 1-cm cubes of tofu
- paper towels
- marking pen

Helpful Hints

- Cut samples as close to class time as possible and cover the samples to keep them from browning.
- Place the cubes of each food on a separate tray and label trays with three-digit numbers, such as 234, 692, 725, and 118.

Expected Data

Results will vary. Students will be surprised that they were unable to distinguish between some of the samples. Consistency and chewiness will probably enable them to distinguish the tofu from the others.

ANSWER KEY

Student Text

● ANSWERS TO QUESTIONS IN TEXT:

p. 38   Both enhance flavors.

p. 40   Examples will vary.

p. 41

A laboratory panel is usually a small, controlled study, while a large consumer panel is usually larger, and often random, given in a supermarket or shopping mall.

p. 44

The word salt comes from the Latin word "salarium." It is related to salaries because Roman soldiers were paid their salaries in salt.

● CHECK YOUR FACTS

1. Sensory evaluation is the scientific evaluation of food using the human senses of sight, smell, taste, and hearing.

2. Appearance, odor, taste, feel in the mouth, and sound.
3. To be unable to distinguish between the flavors of some foods.
4. When it is hot.
5. How a food feels in the mouth.
6. To identify samples during testing to avoid influencing results with the labels used.
7. To keep the testing area as free from distractions as possible by controlling factors such as lighting and temperature.
8. Late morning and midafternoon because they are times when people tend to be most alert and most responsive to sensory testing.
9. Salt.
10. Advertising, brand identity, and cultural heritage.

● CRITICAL THINKING AND PROBLEM SOLVING

1. Sweet and salty foods.
2. They lose their sense of smell which makes it difficult for them to taste.
3. They contain the same flavor-enhancing chemical found in MSG.
4. It would taste sweeter than usual.
5. Coffee and wine are such complex substances that only highly trained experts can evaluate them properly.
6. Warm water dissolves fatty substances better than cool water.
7. Answers will vary but could include: using three-digit numbers to identify samples, having all samples at the same temperature, providing water to tasters to use to rinse their mouths between samples, giving tasters a list of traits they can use in rating the samples.

Student Activity Workbook

● H-2-1: STUDY GUIDE

1. Sight, smell taste, touch and hearing.
2. People.
3. How ripe it is.
4. To add color to a food or drink.
5. It may warn that a food is not safe to eat.
6. Sweet, sour, bitter, salty.
7. Monosodium glutamate.

8. During cooking.
9. Graininess, thickness, brittleness, or chewiness.
10. Tenderness.
11. To encourage people to eat food that is good for them.
12. During production of food.
13. In grocery stores, at shopping malls, or at special research companies.
14. Light, temperature, noise, and odor.
15. By using colored lights.
16. Presenting a good-quality sample before a sample of poor quality, which can lead to a lower rating for the second sample than it might otherwise have gotten.
17. No more than three.
18. Onion, garlic, parsley, oregano, honey, cinnamon.
19. Dairy products, wheat products, exotic foods.
20. Heritage of ancestors, level of hunger, advertising, and brand identity.

● H-2-2: CROSSWORD PUZZLE

Across	Down
1. sensory	2. evaluation
4. laboratory	3. samples
5. booths	6. temperature
7. warm	8. experts
11. atmosphere	9. water
12. food science	10. technology
13. career	15. random
14. contrast	18. digit
16. consumer	19. senses
17. controlled	
20. midafternoon	
21. rinsing	

● H-2-3: NUTRITION AND YOU

1. Sensory appeal.
2. Texture, color, and shape.
3. Appearance, odor, flavor, and mouthfeel.
4. Variety.
5. Boredom.

6. Doctor's supervision.
7. Complete meal formula/liquid protein.
8. Warning label.
9. The ability to taste certain flavors declines.
10. No taste at all, all foods taste the same.

● T-4: WHAT IS SENSORY EVALUATION?

1. appearance
2. odor
3. flavor
4. mouthfeel
5. sound

● *Experiment 2-1:* ODOR RECOGNITION

1. Answers will vary.
2. Answers will vary.
3. The senses are interdependent.

● *Experiment 2-2:* FLAVOR COMPARISON

1. Answers will vary.
2. Answers will vary.
3. Answers will vary.
4. Answers will vary.
5. Sweet, sour, salty, and bitter.

Teacher's Resource Guide

● *Experiment 2-A:* MOUTHFEEL AND SENSORY EVALUATION

1. Answers will vary.
2. Answers will vary.
3. Consistency and chewiness were the most useful traits. Brittleness and thickness were the least useful traits.

Chapter 2: The Scientific Evaluation of Food

WHAT IS SENSORY EVALUATION?

TEXT PAGES 34-47

DIRECTIONS: Fill in the right column with the characteristics of food evaluated by each sense listed in the left column.

Senses Used in Sensory Evaluation	Characteristics of Food Evaluated by Each Sense
Sight	1.
Smell	2.
Taste	3.
Touch	4.
Hearing	5.

EXPERIMENT 2-A
Mouthfeel and Sensory Evaluation

SAFETY: Place your initials under each appropriate symbol to show the safety precautions you need to remember when performing this experiment.

Flavor is actually a combination of several sensations, including odor, taste, appearance, and mouthfeel. Some of the factors that influence mouthfeel are temperature, food shape and form, hot or burning sensations due to spiciness, consistency, chewiness, astringency (sourness), graininess, brittleness, and thickness. In this experiment, you will test the mouthfeel of food samples with similar appearances. You will eliminate odor as much as possible by holding your nose.

PROCEDURE

1. Obtain one sample of each of the four foods being tested. Place each sample on a piece of paper towel that has the number of the sample written on it.
2. Offer the four samples to your laboratory partner, one at a time. Your partner should hold his or her nose. As your partner chews each sample, he or she should write the sample number in the data table and rate the sample

according to the traits listed in the data table. Each trait should be rated high, low, or average. For example, if the food sample is very chewy, "high" would be written in the appropriate space in the data table.
3. After tasting all four samples, your partner should repeat steps 1–2 while you taste the samples and complete your data table.

QUESTIONS

1. What do you think each of the four samples was?
2. Could you detect odor even though you were holding your nose? Why or why not?
3. What mouthfeel traits were most helpful in distinguishing among the four samples? The least useful?

SAMPLE DATA TABLE

Trait	Sample # _____	Sample # _____	Sample # _____	Sample # _____
Chewiness				
Astringency				
Thickness				
Graininess				
Brittleness				
Consistency				
Spiciness				

Basic Science for Food Scientists

TEXT PAGES 48–65

SUGGESTED TIME SCHEDULE

180-day course—8 days.
90-day course—5 days.

STUDENT OBJECTIVES

- Compare and contrast elements and compounds.
- Describe heterogeneous mixtures and homogeneous mixtures and explain their similarities and differences.
- Identify common examples of pure substances and mixtures.
- Describe the parts of an atom.
- Recognize chemical symbols, formulas, and equations and discuss how they are used in food science.
- Explain the differences between ionic and covalent bonds and ionic and covalent compounds.
- Differentiate between chemical and physical changes in food.

CHAPTER SUMMARY

- Matter, anything that has mass and occupies space, is divided into two categories—pure substances and mixtures.
- Elements are the simplest type of pure substance and are represented by symbols.
- A compound is made up of two or more elements chemically bonded together and is shown by a formula.
- Mixtures are composed of two or more substances combined in varying amounts.
- Atoms are the smallest particle of an element that keep the chemical properties of the element.

- Chemical bonds between atoms can be either ionic or covalent, depending on whether electrons are transferred or shared.
- A chemical change is a process where substances become new and different substances.
- Physical changes in a substance involve changes such as size, shape, or phase, but the basic identity of the substance does not change.

BACKGROUND INFORMATION

Chapter 3 contains basic scientific information on elements, compounds, and mixtures. In addition, it briefly explains the symbols, formulas, and equations used to describe these materials and the changes that they undergo during chemical reactions.

Elements, the simplest chemical substances, are represented by one or two letter symbols. When two or more of these elements join together during a combination reaction, a compound is formed. Compounds are represented by the letters of their component elements. When a compound breaks apart in a decomposition reaction, simpler compounds (with fewer elements) or elements are the products.

No matter how complex a chemical reaction is, matter is always conserved. The total mass of the products is always exactly the same as the total mass of the reactants. This law is known as Conservation of Matter: In any chemical change, the total number of atoms of elements remains the same from the beginning to end of the process, regardless of how they rearrange themselves.

When we "balance" chemical equations, we represent on paper what happens to atoms during a reaction. For example, if sulfur trioxide gas, SO_3, dissolves in water, H_2O, sulfuric acid, H_2SO_4 is the product. The chemical equation that correctly represents this combination reaction is:

$$SO_3 + H_2O \rightarrow H_2SO_4$$

We can see that on the left side of this equation there is one sulfur atom represented, two hydrogen atoms, and four oxygen atoms. That is exactly what we find on the right side of the equation as well. This chemical equation is balanced.

On the other hand, if we represent the equation in which hydrogen gas, H_2, and oxygen gas, O_2, combine to form water, H_2O, we find we have a little more work to do. Initially, simply writing the correct symbols and formulas for the substances involved we have:

$$H_2 + O_2 \rightarrow H_2O.$$

This equation shows two hydrogen atoms on the left side of the arrow along with two oxygen atoms. However, on the right (or products side), we find two hydrogen atoms but only one oxygen atom. To correct the problem, we can put coefficients in front of the substances in the equation in such a way that there will be the same number of atoms of each element represented on each side of the equation:

$$2\,H_2 + O_2 \rightarrow 2\,H_2O.$$

Now we have four hydrogen atoms represented on each side of the arrow and two oxygen atoms on each side of the arrow. This process takes practice, but it can be used to balance most chemical equations.

Although there are 92 naturally occurring elements, only a few will be referred to in this course. Foods are complex mixtures of many compounds, which is why there are no written formulas for most foods. Sodium chloride is a rare exception.

Both chemical and physical changes occur during food processing, preservation, and preparation. Often, a combination of changes occurs simultaneously. The scientific concepts described in this chapter will help food science students better understand the changes that occur.

Teacher's Resource Guide
REPRODUCIBLE MATERIALS

T-5:   Ionic and Covalent Bonding

ACTIVITIES

1. Discuss with students the classification of matter as shown on page 50 of *Food Science*.
2. Show film: "Chemistry: Elements, Compounds, and Mixtures," CORO, 1983 (20 minutes). Discuss the differences among elements, compounds, and mixtures.
3. Review chemical symbols with students. Explain how symbols are combined to make formulas representing compounds and how formulas are used in chemical equations. Discuss with students the differences between the numbers used in front of formulas to denote the number of molecules and the subscripts used to show the relative number of atoms in a compound.
4. Have students prepare a set of "Symbol Bingo" cards. The cards should contain 9 or 16 symbols of elements frequently used in food science. Students can use a paper marker to cover the corresponding symbol when the name of an element is called. The first person to cover a horizontal, vertical, or diagonal row of symbols wins the round.
5. Use **T-5: Ionic and Covalent Bonding** to help students understand the two types of bonds and how they occur. (This is printed in the *Guide* and in the *Student Activity Workbook*.)
6. Demonstrate chemical and physical changes for students. Chemical changes could include burning paper, allowing a sliced apple to brown, and changing the color of grape or red cabbage juice by adding lemon juice or vinegar. Physical changes could include folding paper, breaking chalk, and melting ice.
7. In preparation for **Experiment 3-1: Mass and Volume of Beans**, demonstrate techniques to be used by students during the experiment.
8. In preparation for **Experiment 3-2: Physical and Chemical Changes**, demonstrate the use of the watch glass to evaporate liquid.

OVERVIEW OF EXPERIMENTS

- **Experiment 3-1: MASS AND VOLUME OF BEANS**

Time Required

Day 1—20 minutes
Day 2—25 minutes

Objective

Students will use the balances to determine mass while determining the volume of irregular objects using the displacement of water.

Equipment

- 6 triple beam balances/3 electronic balances
- 12 100-mL graduated cylinders
- 12 100-mL beakers
- 12 large test tube brushes
- tray

Supplies

- 0.5-kg packages of three kinds of beans.
- masking tape
- marking pen

Helpful Hints

- Do not use lima beans since they are too soft to handle by the second day. White, navy, pinto, black, or kidney beans are all satisfactory choices.
- Since the beans tend to stick to the bottom of the graduated cylinders, remind students to be certain to transfer all the beans from the cylinders to the beakers.
- Using a labeled tray for each class period makes it easy to store the beakers and for students to locate their samples on the second day of the experiment.
- Check the beakers before leaving school in the evening and again when you arrive in the morning to be sure that no beans are exposed to the air. Add water to any beaker in which the liquid level has dropped below the level of the beans.
- Remind students to wash the glassware carefully at the end of the experiment because the beans tend to leave a starch residue on the glass.

Laboratory Simplification

Use one type of bean or use only 25 beans.

Laboratory Enrichment

Calculate the density of dried beans and compare with the density of soaked beans.

Expected Data

Students should indicate the variety of beans used. The following data is for small red beans. Generally the white or navy beans do not double in size, while pinto and kidney beans more than double.

Measurements	Dried Beans	Soaked Beans
Mass of empty beaker	63.3 g	63.3 g
Mass of beaker and 50 beans	80.3 g	98.7 g
Mass of 50 beans	17.0 g	35.4 g
Mass of one bean	0.35 g	0.71 g
Volume of water in graduated cylinder	20.0 mL	40.0 mL
Volume of water and beans	33.0 mL	72.0 mL
Volume of 50 beans	13.0 mL	32.0 mL
Volume of one bean	0.26 mL	0.64 mL
Change in mass for one bean	—	.35 g
Change in volume for one bean	—	.38 mL

• Experiment 3-2: PHYSICAL AND CHEMICAL CHANGES

Time Required

40 minutes

Objective

Students will dissolve solids in water and vinegar (an acid) to compare physical and chemical changes that occur during dissolving.

Equipment

- 12 magnifying glasses
- 12 25-mL graduated cylinders
- 12 100-mL beakers
- 12 watch glasses
- safety goggles for all students

Supplies

- sodium chloride
- sodium bicarbonate
- 120 mL white vinegar

Helpful Hints

- It is not necessary to evaporate more than 1–2 mL of each solution. Using more liquid will only lengthen the time required for the experiment.
- The crystal shape of sodium bicarbonate is that of a monoclinic prism. This shape can only be observed under a microscope.
- Warn students not to lean over the watch glass as the liquid evaporates. As the solid begins to crystallize, some spattering may occur. Heating the solution slowly will help minimize spattering.
- Due to the rapid rate of crystallization in this procedure, few observable cubic crystals of sodium chloride form. Therefore, you may want to leave one watch glass and liquid in a safe place so the water can evaporate slowly. When this is done, cubic crystals (like those observed at the beginning of the experiment) will be produced.

Laboratory Simplification

None.

Laboratory Enrichment

Also test sucrose and baking powder.

Expected Data

Samples	Original	After Evaporation
Sodium chloride Appearance	cubic crystals	nonuniform crystals
Taste	salty	salty
Sodium bicarbonate Appearance	white powder	not quite as powdery
Behavior with vinegar	produces gas (CO_2)	no gas produced

ANSWER KEY

Student Text

● ANSWERS TO QUESTIONS IN TEXT:

p. 50
Aluminum is an element. Oil and vinegar salad dressing is a heterogeneous mixture.

p. 52 6×10^{36} atoms.

p. 53   Protons are positive.

p. 54   H, N, O, and Cl.

p. 61
1. Melting is a physical change.
2. No, cooling is a physical change which would not alter nutritional value.

● CHECK YOUR FACTS

1. A pure substance is made up of only one kind of material and has definite properties. A mixture is composed of two or more substances, which can be combined in varying amounts.
2. Elements.
3. An element is the simplest type of pure substance from which all other materials are formed. A compound is made of two or more elements chemically attached together.
4. A solution.
5. Outside the nucleus.
6. **a.** S   **b.** P   **c.** H.
7. **a.** carbon   **b.** nitrogen   **c.** chlorine   **d.** calcium   **e.** sodium.
8. **a.** NaCl   **b.** H_2O **c.** $C_6H_{12}O_6$.
9. Reactants, yield arrow, products.
10. Electrons are transferred in ionic compounds and shared in covalent compounds.
11. In chemical changes, new and different substances are formed. During physical changes, the basic chemical nature of the substance is not changed.

● CRITICAL THINKING AND PROBLEM SOLVING

1. Mixtures, because there are many compounds present that do not occur in exactly the same proportions. Therefore, there is no chemical formula for beans of any kind.

2. **a.** heterogeneous **b.** homogeneous **c.** homogeneous **d.** homogeneous **e.** heterogeneous.
3. **a.** sodium-1, chloride-1 **b.** hydrogen-2, oxygen-1 **c.** hydrogen-2, sulfur-1, oxygen-4 **d.** hydrogen-2 **e.** carbon-6, hydrogen-12, oxygen-6.
4. 3.

Student Activity Workbook

● H-3-1: STUDY GUIDE

1. property	20. carbon
2. elements, compounds	21. chlorine
3. elements	22. calcium
4. carbon	23. oxygen
5. heterogeneous	24. nitrogen
6. atom	25. 1 sulfur, 2 oxygen, 3 atoms
7. outside	26. 1 sulfur, 3 oxygen, 4 atoms
8. protons, neutrons	27. 1 sulfur, 4 oxygen, 7 atoms
9. equation	28. 2
10. chemical bond	29. 2
11. ions	30. 3
12. shared	31. 1
13. chemical	32. 3
14. physical	33. A
15. P	34. D
16. S	35. E
17. H	36. C
18. Al	
19. Fe	

● H-3-2: CROSSWORD PUZZLE

Across	Down
4. homogeneous	1. formula
7. Al	2. Fe
9. heterogeneous	3. sugar
11. atom	5. Na
12. matter	6. water
14. covalent	8. solutions
17. proton	10. compound
18. element	12. mixture
19. pure	13. electron
	15. sodium
	16. salt

● H-3-3: ELEMENT MATCHING

1. hydrogen	11. Mn
2. C	12. iron
3. nitrogen	13. Zn
4. O	14. potassium
5. fluorine	15. copper
6. k	16. I
7. magnesium	17. chlorine
8. Na	18. S
9. calcium	19. nickel
10. Mo	20. Cr

● H-3-4: NUTRITION AND YOU

1. Melting is a physical change.
2. Cooling is a physical change.
3. No, a physical change such as cooling would not alter the nutritional value of the potatoes.
4. Ripening is a chemical change.
5. When you chew food you grind it with your teeth, which is a physical change. At the same time saliva in your mouth begins to dissolve the food, which is a chemical change.
6. The changes that take place in food in the mouth make the nutrients in food available for use by the body.
7. Generally, chemical changes alter the nutritional value of food.
8. Potatoes lose nutrients to the water when they are boiled. Using this water in making gravy provides an opportunity for these nutrients to be consumed rather than wasted.
9. Answers will vary. Possible examples include hard-boiled eggs and potatoes baked and served in their skins.
10. Answers will vary. Students may state that some foods are not safe to eat raw or cannot be digested by humans unless they are cooked.

● T-5: IONIC AND COVALENT BONDING

1. ionic
2. covalent

● Experiment 3-1: MASS AND VOLUME OF BEANS

1. Information in data table.
2. Information in data table.
3. Information in data table.
4. Information in data table.
5. Amount of beans needed since they will increase in volume, a container large enough to hold the increased volume is needed, and the amount of liquid needed in the recipe.

● Experiment 3-2: PHYSICAL AND CHEMICAL CHANGES

1. Bubbles of gas were given off when the baking soda dissolved.
2. Yes, the solid had the same taste as the original solid known to be sodium chloride. Some of the crystals had the same shape as the original, although these were hard to see without a microscope. A physical change.
3. No, because it did not produce bubbles when vinegar was added to it like the baking soda did. A chemical change.

Chapter 3: Basic Science for Food Scientists

IONIC AND COVALENT BONDING

TEXT PAGES 48–65

DIRECTIONS: In the spaces given, identify the type of bonding shown in each illustration.

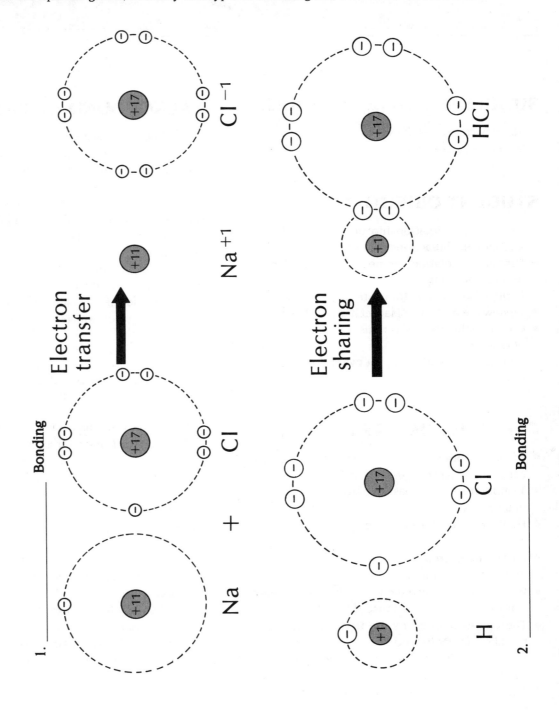

CHAPTER 4

Energy

TEXT PAGES 66—79

SUGGESTED TIME SCHEDULE

180-day course—9 days.
90-day course—4 days.

STUDENT OBJECTIVES

- Describe the relationship of energy and physical and chemical reactions.
- Discuss the relationship between molecular motion and temperature.
- Explain how heat is transferred.
- Review the meaning of latent heat in phase changes.
- Compare the effect of various temperatures on rates of reaction.
- Analyze the relationship between food intake and body weight.

CHAPTER SUMMARY

- Energy is either released or absorbed in all physical or chemical changes.
- Temperature is a measure of the molecular motion in a substance.
- Heat is transferred through conduction and convection.
- Latent heat creates a phase change without an increase in temperature.
- Heating a substance increases the rate of reaction, while cooling the substance decreases it.
- The energy needed by the body is obtained from the kilocalories in food.
- Food varies in kilocalories depending on the nutrients in the food.
- The amount of kilocalories consumed affects weight gain and loss.

BACKGROUND INFORMATION

In Chapter 4, students study the importance of energy—heat in particular—in physical and chemical changes. They will learn how heat is transferred and that energy known as latent heat is stored in molecules when substances melt or boil. This latent heat is then releases when these substances freeze or condense. the chapter also includes information on how the body uses energy.

In discussing temperature and cooking rate, point out that pressure cookers reduce the required cooking time. They do this by using pressure to raise the boiling point of water, which increases cooking rate.

Teacher's Resource Guide
REPRODUCIBLE MATERIALS

T-6: Do You Balance Activity and Food Intake?
E-4-A: Heat Transfer Through Metal

ACTIVITIES

1. Introduce the concept of energy by showing the film "Molecular Motion," MOLA, 1962 (13 minutes).
2. Discuss with students the various types of energy, how energy is transferred, and what happens during and after heat transfer.
3. Prepare a typical custard recipe to illustrate heat transfer by convection and conduction.

4. Different substances transfer heat at different rates. If students are not going to do **Experiment 4-A: Heat Transfer Through Metal**, demonstrate the differences in heat transfer in several fry pans.

5. To demonstrate a phase change, fill a wax-coated paper cup with water. Heat it directly on the stove until the water boils. As long as there is water in the cup, the temperature of the cup and water remain at 100°C, so the cup does not burn. This occurs because the heat energy is transferred to the water to keep it boiling.

6. Discuss with students the effect of temperature and surface area in food preparation. In what foods would these factors be especially significant? Examples could include french fries vs. baked potatoes, steak vs. a roast, whole carrots vs. sliced carrots, etc.

7. Discuss with students how the surface area exposed during cooking affects the nutritional value of food. Explain cooking techniques that help preserve nutritional value and those that destroy nutritional value.

8. Use the article, "Cooking with Steam," *Chem Matters*, February 1987, pages 17–19, as a reading assignment or as an additional source of short experiments that students can carry out either in school or at home.

9. Discuss with students the difference between calories and kilocalories and how kilocalories are used by the body. Use **T-6: Do You Balance Activity and Food Intake?** to help students understand how food intake and activity/exercise affect weight gain and loss. It is printed in the *Guide* only.

10. Provide or have students locate copies of popular diets for weight loss. Have students analyze the diets and decide whether they think the diets would be healthy for people following them.

11. Ask a physician, psychiatric nurse, or a dietitian to discuss eating disorders and how they are treated.

12. In preparation for the experiments, prepare raw potato cubes, ones that are partially cooked, and ones that are fully cooked. Pass these cubes around the class so students can get a feel for the ease with which toothpicks will penetrate potatoes at each of these degrees of doneness. Otherwise, reported results will vary tremendously because students do not know how to distinguish when the potato cubes are fully cooked.

EXTENSION ACTIVITY

Have students conduct **Experiment 4-A: Heat Transfer Through Metal**.

OVERVIEW OF EXPERIMENTS

● *Experiment* 4-1: EFFECT OF TEMPERATURE ON COOKING RATE

Time Required

45 minutes

Objective

Students will observe the effect of temperature on the rate of cooking.

Equipment

- 12 100-mL graduated cylinders
- 12 400-mL beakers
- 12 thermometers
- 12 paring knives
- 12 ring stands
- 12 utility clamps
- 12 1-hole stoppers

Supplies

- 6 potatoes
- wooden toothpicks
- 12 2.5-cm squares cut from index cards

Helpful Hints

- Demonstrate how to set up a ring stand and utility clamp with a one-hole stopper in the clamp. Insert the thermometer into the rubber stopper so it is supported with the bulb slightly above the bottom of a beaker. Use glycerin or another lubricant when inserting the thermometer to avoid breaking it. Supporting the thermometer in this manner produces more accurate results.
- Time is saved and the size of the potato cubes used is standardized if students use 2.5-cm squares cut from index cards as a guide in cutting the potato cubes.
- Generally, half of an average-sized potato is needed per laboratory group. Do not cut the potato cubes in advance since they discolor and dry out quickly.

Cut the potatoes in half before you distribute them to the students for the experiment.

- Have students place their data on the chalkboard so that an average can be calculated for the time required to fully cook the cubes at each temperature.

Laboratory Simplification

None.

Laboratory Enrichment

Try at temperatures between 60 and 90 degrees.

Expected Data

In 90°C water, the potato cube should be completely done in 10.5 minutes. In 100°C water, the potato cube should be completely done in 8 minutes.

● Experiment 4-2: EFFECT OF SURFACE AREA ON COOKING RATE

Time Required

45 minutes

Objective

Students will observe the effect of surface area on cooking rate.

Equipment

- 12 100-mL graduated cylinders
- 12 400-mL beakers
- 12 paring knives

Supplies

- 6 potatoes
- wooden toothpicks
- 12 2.5-cm squares cut from index cards

Helpful Hints

- Virtually the same preliminary steps are required for this experiment as for Experiment 4-1. The 2.5-cm squares cut from index cards are again useful.
- Demonstrate how to cut the original potato cube into 4 and 27 equal-sized smaller cubes.
- Point out how the results of this experiment would be useful to someone who was trying to prepare a dish like potato salad in a hurry.

- Students often enjoy eating the potato cubes after this experiment.

Laboratory Simplification

Use variations 1 and 3 only.

Laboratory Enrichment

Repeat experiment with sweet potatoes or turnips.

Expected Data

The 2.5-cm cubes should be completely done in 9 minutes. The 4 small cubes should be completely done in 6 minutes. The 27 small cubes should be completely done in 3 minutes.

● Experiment 4-A: HEAT TRANSFER THROUGH METAL

Note: The procedure for this experiment is printed only in the *Teacher's Resource Guide*.

Time Required

Varies with the number of pans used. Most laboratory groups can test 45 pans in a class period.

Objective

Students will observe that, with different metals, the rate and evenness with which heat is conducted varies.

Equipment

- Use whichever of the following fry pans are available. Students can trade pans if there are not enough pans available for each laboratory group to have a complete set for testing.
  - aluminum fry pan
  - copper lined with stainless steel fry pan
  - porcelain enamel cast iron fry pan
  - copper-bottom stainless steel fry pan
  - cast aluminum fry pan
  - cast iron fry pan
  - stainless steel fry pan
  - aluminum fry pan lined with a nonstick coating

Supplies

- flour
- oil

Helpful Hints

- Prior to the experiment, explain to students the importance of removing excess flour before heating the pans.
- Each laboratory group must do the entire experiment on the same heating unit for their data to have meaning. This means students can heat only one pan at a time.
- Fry pans made from other metals can be used. Examples might include copper/tin, stainless steel with an aluminum bottom, or stainless steel with a copper core.

Expected Data

Data will vary depending on the heating units.

ANSWER KEY
Student Text

● ANSWERS TO QUESTIONS IN TEXT:

p. 68
A Calorie is a kilocalorie and is 1000 calories.

p. 71   Water molecules

p. 74   Answers will vary.

p. 75   Rice

p. 76
Both bulimia and anorexia nervosa are eating disorders. An individual with anorexia nervosa is obsessed with being thin, often placing him or herself on a starvation diet. Bulimia is different in that individuals eat large amounts of food, but then either make themselves vomit or take excessive amounts of laxatives to purge their system. Both disorders are dangerous to one's health.

● CHECK YOUR FACTS

1. It is either released or absorbed.
2. Heat, because it is involved in cooking food.
3. The amount of heat energy required to raise the temperature of 1 g water 1°C. A kilocalorie is equal to 1000 calories.
4. It increases also.
5. From a warmer material to a cooler one.

6. The energy flowing to the ice is used to separate the molecules, rather than to speed them up (which would raise the temperature).
7. It speeds up molecules, causing them to collide more often. Because the molecules are moving faster when they collide, they are more likely to react.
8. Fats, protein, carbohydrates.
9. People gain weight when they eat more kilocalories than are burned by the body. They lose weight when they eat fewer kilocalories than are burned by the body.
10. Rice.
11. 3500 kcal.

● CRITICAL THINKING AND PROBLEM SOLVING

1. From the liquid water to the ice.
2. The microwaves affect water molecules in the food sample to a depth of 57.5 cm, while heat only affects the surface molecules and then must be slowly transmitted throughout the food sample.
3. Hot tea—the heat speeds up the rate of reaction.
4. Powdered sugar—it has more surface area per gram of solid.
5. They cook faster than thick ones.
6. The number of kilocalories in a candy bar won't make a person fat if the person exercises enough to burn off those kilocalories.
7. Their bodies must use more calories to maintain a healthy body temperature because of their colder surroundings.
8. Both are eating disorders in people who believe they are overweight. Anorexics simply don't eat, while bulemics eat but then purge themselves with laxatives or by vomiting.

Student Activity Workbook

● H-4-1: STUDY GUIDE

1. A kilocalorie or Calorie.
2. The metric unit of heat flow—it is equal to 0.239 cal.
3. Absolute zero.
4. Gas.
5. They vibrate and rotate.
6. The energy needed to raise the temperature of 1 g of a substance 1°C.
7. In calories.

8. The transfer of energy from particle to particle through molecular collisions.
9. The transfer of energy through the motion of fluids or gases.
10. From the water to the surroundings.
11. It remains constant.
12. It separates the liquid water molecules.
13. Temperature.
14. The molecules in the food must collide with each other.
15. The higher the temperature, the more often they collide.
16. It increases.
17. It doubles.
18. It slows it down.
19. It increases.
20. From the sun, the air, and the soil.
21. From the nutrients in the food they eat.
22. Ice cream.
23. Eat 500 fewer kcals a day than your body normally requires.
24. An eating disorder where the person is on a starvation diet.
25. Vomiting causes a loss of hydrochloric acid from the stomach, which leads to a loss of potassium. Extreme potassium loss can lead to heart failure.

● H-4-2: MAGIC SQUARE

A.	1	D.	5	G.	9
B.	6	E.	7	H.	2
C.	8	F.	3	I.	4

The magic number is 15.

● H-4-3: NUTRITION AND YOU

1. Answers will vary depending upon students weight.
2. Answers will vary.
3. Answers will vary.
4. Answers will vary.

5. Both bulimia and anorexia nervosa are eating disorders. An individual with anorexia nervosa is obsessed with being thin. They often place themselves on a starvation diet. Bulimia is different in that individuals eat large amounts of food, but then either make themselves vomit or take excessive amounts of laxatives to purge their system. Both disorders are dangerous to one's health.

● *Experiment 4-1:* EFFECT OF TEMPERATURE ON COOKING RATE

1. Answered from data table and class data.
2. Depends on class data.
3. Depends on class data.
4. The higher temperatures caused an increased rate of chemical reaction (i.e., the potato cooked faster).

● *Experiment 4-2:* EFFECT OF SURFACE AREA ON COOKING RATE

1. It was the same in each beaker.
2. Yes, the smaller the size of the cubes, the shorter the cooking time.
3. Because there was more surface area where immediate reactions occurred and because heat had to be transferred less distance to the center of the cube, the smaller cubes cooked faster than the larger ones.

Teacher's Resource Guide

● *Experiment 4-A:* HEAT TRANSFER THROUGH METAL

1. Answers will vary depending on pans used.
2. Answers will vary depending on pans used.
3. Answers will vary.

Do You Balance Activity and Food Intake?

EXPERIMENT 4-A
Heat Transfer Through Metal

Heat transfer through cookware takes place when food is cooked on a surface unit on a stove. To ensure that food being cooked is done evenly, the materials used to make cookware need to conduct heat rapidly and evenly. In this experiment, you will test several fry pans to discover which ones conduct heat the most quickly and evenly.

PROCEDURE

1. Lightly grease and flour the pan to be tested. Remove the excess flour by turning the pan upside down over the sink and thumping the bottom of the pan with the flat of your hand.
2. On medium heat, preheat the large heating unit on the stove for 2 minutes. Use the same burner on the same setting for each pan tested.
3. Place the pan on the burner and time how long it takes for the flour coating to turn a light golden brown.
4. In your data table, record the time it took for browning to occur. Note whether the flour coating is evenly browned or browned only in spots. Record your observations in the data table.
5. When the pan is cool, thoroughly wash and dry it.
6. Repeat steps 1–5 with each pan to be tested. If necessary, trade pans with other laboratory groups until you have tested all the pans specified by your teacher.

QUESTIONS

1. Which pan heated the fastest?
2. Which pan conducted heat most evenly?
3. Which pan do you think is the best one to use for cooking? Why?

SAMPLE DATA TABLE

Metal(s) Used in Pan	Time Needed for Browning	Evenness of Browning

CHAPTER 5

Acids and Bases

TEXT PAGES 80–95

SUGGESTED TIME SCHEDULE

180-day course—7 days.
90-day course—4 days.

STUDENT OBJECTIVES

- Discuss what happens when water ionizes and how ionization relates to the formation of acids and bases.
- Identify the properties of acids and bases.
- Describe the pH scale and how it is used.
- Use indicators to measure the pH of solutions.
- Define atomic mass and mole and analyze the relationship between them.
- Explain how molarity is calculated.
- Describe the importance of pH in digestion and blood.
- Discuss ways pH is related to the properties of food, its safety, and its freshness.

CHAPTER SUMMARY

- Acids have a sour taste, change the color of indicators, and neutralize bases.
- Bases have a bitter taste, feel slippery, change the color of indicators, and neutralize acids.
- The pH of a solution can be measured by a pH meter, indicator paper, or titration.
- A mole is 6.02×10^{23} items and is the unit of measure scientists use to relate the number of atoms in an element or molecules in a compound to a mass in grams.
- Molarity is the number of moles of a solute in a liter of solution.

- The pH of the fluids in the stomach and small intestine is an important factor in the digestion of food.
- Buffers help regulate blood pH to prevent excessive buildup of hydrogen or hydroxide ions.
- The pH of a food can affect its properties, safety, and freshness.

BACKGROUND INFORMATION

In Chapter 5 students learn about the crucial role that acids and bases play—both in food preparation and preservation and in the body. Students are introduced to the properties of acids and bases and how the pH scale is used to express the strength of these substances.

The pH scale was developed by a bottling plant scientist who was responsible for maintaining the correct acidity in the carbonated beverages produced at the plant. This scale is now used by scientists throughout the world. The "p" in the term stands for the power of ten and the "H" stands for the concentration of hydrogen ions, "H^+" (or, more correctly, the hydronium ion, H_3O^+). The formal definition of pH is "the negative of the logarithm of the hydrogen ion concentration."

While pH meters are the most accurate means of measuring pH, their use is generally limited in science laboratories because of cost. However, they are getting smaller and cheaper, so it may be economical to have them in the laboratory in the future.

Most foods are at least slightly acidic. Few foods are basic. Some foods can serve as natural pH indicators. These include red cabbage, blueberry and blackberry juice, and tea.

Carbon dioxide gas makes solutions more acidic because some of the gas molecules react with water to form carbonic acid. The carbonic acid ionizes to form hydrogen ions, causing the solution to be acidic. The reactions involved are shown below.

$$CO_2 + H_2O \rightarrow H_2CO_3 \rightarrow H^+ + HCO_3^-$$

The acidity of carbonated beverages varies depending on the level of carbonation.

To get accurate answers to Question 6 in "Critical Thinking and Problem Solving," you may need to provide students with recipes that use baking soda as a leavening agent. Baking powder is a source of both acid and base, while baking soda is a base. Recipes which use baking soda normally contain a separate acidic ingredient, such as sour milk, lemon juice, etc.

In nature, there are three ways to measure how much of something you have: by number, by mass, and by volume. In chemistry, scientists also measure in terms of moles.

A mole is the amount of substance in grams equal to the atomic mass of a substance. So, 12 g of carbon (whose atomic number is 12) contains the same number of atoms of carbon as 1 g of hydrogen (whose atomic number is one). That number is 6.02×10^{23}, one mole.

Molarity is the number of moles of solute dissolved in 1 L of solution. To prepare a solution of a given molarity, one must determine a proper amount of substance to dissolve in a proper amount of solution. For example, to prepare 2.0 L of a 0.1 M solution of sodium hydroxide, NaOH, the method would be as follows:

1. First, determine the mass of one mole of sodium hydroxide by adding the molar masses of the compound's elements: Na = 23 g/mole, O = 16 g/mole and H = 1 g/mole. One mole of NaOH would have a mass of (23 + 16 + 1 =) 40 g.

2. Then, determine how many moles of NaOH are needed. To prepare 2 liters of a 0.1 M solution, one needs (2 L × 0.1 mole/L =) 0.2 moles of NaOH.

3. If one mole of NaOH has a mass of 40 g, then the amount of sodium hydroxide required would be (0.2 moles × 40 g/mole =) 8 g.

4. Dissolve these 8 g in enough water to make 2.0 L of solution.

When diluting an existing solution to a lesser concentration, use the equation M1 × V1 = M2 × V2 to determine how much more of the concentrated solution to add. M1 is the molarity of the solution and V1 is its volume. M2 is the molarity that you want to achieve and V2 is the volume of solution you will end up with. The equation is balanced because the same number of moles of substance will be the same. For example, if you want to dilute an acidic solution, to a

certain molarity, the number of moles of acid solution will be the same before and after adding solution.

You can use a similar formula for neutralization, too. To gain a neutral pH of 7, the number of moles of acidic hydrogen must be equal to the basic hydroxide ions. The mathematical equation for neutralization is Ma × Va = Mb × Vb (where a stands for acid and b for base).

Teacher's Resource Guide
REPRODUCIBLE MATERIALS

T-7:   Understanding Concentration
E-5-A: Using Red Cabbage to Identify Acids and Bases
E-5-B: Temperature Change and the pH of Carbonated Beverages

ACTIVITIES

1. Introduce students to the topic of acids and bases by showing the film: "Chemistry: Acids, Bases, and Salts," CORO, 1983 (20 minutes). Discuss the properties of acids and bases with students.

2. Explain the concept of pH to students. Demonstrate the use of a pH meter and indicator paper.

3. Have students test the pH of the local tap water. It will probably be acidic with a pH of 5–7. If students live in housing with home wells, have them bring water samples to class for testing. Discuss how carbon dioxide and mineral salts in water affect pH.

4. Explain titration and neutralization. Demonstrate how titration is done. Stress the precise nature of titration and the importance of accurate measurements. Be sure to model good safety practices by wearing safety goggles during the demonstration.

5. From powdered drink mix, make a container of normal-strength drink. In addition, make an identical-sized container of very dilute drink. Have students taste the sample and describe the difference they notice. Explain how the two samples were made—that the normal-strength drink was of a much stronger concentration than the dilute drink. Use **T-7: Understanding Concentration** to reinforce the meaning of concentration. (It is printed in the *Guide* only.) Have students give other examples of varying concentrations in specific foods—the amount of cheese in macaroni

and cheese, the number of nuts in butter pecan ice cream, the amount of grapes in a mixed fruit salad, etc.

6. Invite a physician or physiologist to speak to the class on the role of pH in the body and in digestion.

7. Discuss with students how pH affects foods and food preparation. Give specific examples, such as the curdling of homemade tomato soup, the pH changes in eggs as they are stored, the quality of cake crumbs as related to basicity, etc.

8. If possible, show examples of food spoilage and identify whether it is caused by bacteria, yeast, or mold. Discuss how the pH of a food affects the type of spoilage it experiences.

9. If you do not plan to have students perform **Experiment 5-A: Using Red Cabbage to Identify Acids and Bases**, demonstrate the effect of acids and bases on red cabbage, blackberry, or blueberry juice. A cleanser, which is basic, and lemon juice or vinegar can be used. The juice will be greenish as the pH goes above 7, then will turn bluish as it becomes more basic. The juice will be reddish when acid is added.

10. If you do not plan to have students perform **Experiment 5-B: Temperature Change and the pH of Carbonated Beverages**, discuss the changes that occur in carbonated beverages as they "go flat." As the carbon dioxide dissolved in the liquid escapes, the acidity of the liquid decreases and the pH increases. What effect does this process have on flavor, mouthfeel, etc.?

EXTENSION ACTIVITIES

1. Have student conduct **Experiment 5-A: Using Red Cabbage to Identify Acids and Bases**. Students can carry out a similar experiment at home with grape or blackberry juice.

2. Have students conduct **Experiment 5-B: Temperature Change and the pH of Carbonated Beverages**.

OVERVIEW OF EXPERIMENTS

● *Experiment 5-1:* THE pH OF COMMON FOODS

Time Required

45 minutes

Objective

Students will determine the pH of common foods and food ingredients.

Equipment

- 84 test tubes
- 12 test tube racks

Supplies

- pHydrion paper 1–11 range
- labels or grease pencils
- deionized water
- white vinegar (5 percent acetic acid)
- sodium bicarbonate
- 6 egg whites
- honey
- molasses
- buttermilk
- lemon juice
- cream of tartar
- lemon-lime soda
- cranberry-apple juice
- milk
- powdered orange drink

Helpful Hints

- You should be able to get deionized water from the science department. If not, distilled water can be purchased at most pharmacies and some grocery stores.
- It is easiest to mix the powdered orange drink in advance. One 250-mL serving will be enough for all laboratory groups.
- Be sure to mention to students that they need to save test tubes 3 and 4 to combine in step 3. Stress that it is important to thoroughly mix the solutions in step 3 before testing the pH.
- If you do not have enough test tubes, 50-mL beakers or 28-g paper cups will work well.

Laboratory Simplification

Do fewer samples.

Laboratory Enrichment

Students select substances at home to check and report.

Expected Data

Test Tube Number	Solution	pH
1	tap water	5–7
2	deionized water	7
3	vinegar (5% acetic acid)	3
4	sodium bicarbonate (a few crystals) dissolved in deionized water	8
5	egg white	9
6	5 mL honey dissolved in tap water	4
7	5 mL molasses dissolved in tap water	4
8	buttermilk	4
9	lemon juice	3
10	cream of tartar (a few grains) dissolved in tap water	3
11	lemon-lime soda	4
12	cranberry-apple juice	3
13	milk	6.5
14	powdered orange drink dissolved in tap water	4
3–4	mixture of test tubes 3 and 4	4.5

● Experiment 5-2: NEUTRALIZATION

Time Required

45 minutes

Objective

Students will neutralize the acetic acid in vinegar with a 1.0 M solution of sodium hydroxide.

Equipment

- 12 250-mL Erlenmeyer flasks
- 24 burets—if you do not have enough burets for each laboratory group to have two, one dispensing buret for each brand of vinegar is sufficient. Students can take their flasks to these burets, obtain the vinegar they need, and return to their laboratory stations. In this case, 15–16 burets are needed.

Supplies

- 3–4 brands of vinegar
- 1 liter of 1.0 M sodium hydroxide solution (40 g NaOH per liter of solutions)
- phenolphthalein solution (2–3 small dropping bottles). Prepare phenolphthalein solution 1 g to 100 mL alcohol.

Helpful Hints

- It is best to use white vinegar, although the color change can be observed in cider vinegar as well.
- To prepare the sodium hydroxide solution, mass 40 g solid sodium hydroxide. Dissolve the massed solid in deionized water and then add enough additional water so the final volume of the solution is exactly 1 L.
- All brands of vinegar should give similar results since, by law, all brands must contain a set amount of acetic acid in water.

Laboratory Simplification

Use only two brands of vinegar.

Laboratory Enrichment

Titrate lemon juice.

Expected Data

Using 20 mL vinegar and 1.0 M sodium hydroxide. It should take 16–17 mL base to neutralize the vinegar.

● Experiment 5-A: USING RED CABBAGE TO IDENTIFY ACIDS AND BASES

Note: The procedure for this experiment is printed only in the *Teacher's Resource Guide*.

Time Required

30 minutes

Objective

Students will prepare a chemical indicator and use it to identify solutions as acidic or basic.

Equipment

- 12 400-mL beakers
- 12 knives
- 12 medicine droppers
- 12 10-mL graduated cylinders
- 84 test tubes
- 12 test tube racks

Supplies

- red cabbage
- white distilled vinegar
- sodium bicarbonate
- 6 egg whites
- lemon-lime soda or other colorless soft drink
- unknown acid—lemon juice, water and cream of tartar, water and honey, etc.
- unknown base—water and detergent, water and household ammonia, water and cleanser, or sodium bicarbonate solution

Helpful Hints

- This experiment is appealing to students because it allows them to see a common substance change color in the same manner as a commercial indicator as it comes in contact with solutions of various pHs.
- This experiment can be combined with **Experiment 5-1: The pH of Common Foods** by having students prepare the cabbage indicator at the beginning of the combined experiment. The students would then test each solution with the cabbage indicator AFTER they test it with indicator paper.

Expected Data

Solution	pH	Color of Indicator
vinegar	3	red
lemon-lime soda	4	red
tap water	5–7	purple
sodium bicarbonate	8	green/blue
egg white	9	green/blue
unknown acid	varies	red
unknown base	varies	green to blue
mixed unknowns	varies	varies

● Experiment 5-B: TEMPERATURE CHANGE AND THE pH OF CARBONATED BEVERAGES

Note: The procedure for this experiment is printed only in the *Teacher's Resource Guide*.

Time Required

25 minutes

Objective

Students will observe that as the carbonation level of the solution decreases, its pH increases.

Equipment

- 12 test tubes
- 12 250-mL beakers
- 12 thermometers

Supplies

- colorless carbonated beverage
- pHydrion paper

Helpful Hints

- Plain seltzer or club soda show the largest change in pH in this experiment because they do not contain citric acid as a flavoring. Beverages containing citric acid remain more acidic even though the carbonic acid level decreases as the carbon dioxide leaves the solution.

- Having the carbonated beverage chilled allows students to get the lowest possible value for the first pH reading.

Expected Data

Results will vary depending on the beverage used. In all cases, an increase in pH occurs. Lowest pH values will range from 3–5, while the highest value to which the pH rises is generally about 6.

ANSWER KEY
Student Text

● ANSWERS TO QUESTIONS IN TEXT:

p. 83
A solution of pH 3 is acidic.

p. 84
Gastric juice from the stomach is the most acidic.

p. 86 $N_2 = 28$, $O_2 = 32$

p. 89
1. Vitamins and minerals are absorbed into the body without being chemically changed.
2. The stomach lining secretes a thick, slimy mucus to protect itself from stomach acid.

p. 90
The blackberry juice will turn blue.

● CHECK YOUR FACTS

1. $H_2O \leftrightarrow H^+ + OH^-$.
2. Have a sour taste, change the color of indicators, and neutralize bases.
3. Feel slippery, change the color of indicators, taste bitter, and neutralize acids.
4. 7.
5. Acidic.
6. 7.
7. Red.
8. When neutralization occurs.
9. Carbon—12; sulfur—32.1; calcium—40.1.
10. Oxygen—16 g; phosphorus—31 g; iron—55.8 g; carbon dioxide—44 g.

11. So that protein can be digested.
12. 7.4.
13. 4.6 or less.
14. Carbon dioxide escapes through the egg shell.
15. 4–7.

● CRITICAL THINKING AND PROBLEM SOLVING

1. The gases and solids dissolved in it.
2. A base.
3. The vinegar—it takes less of it to neutralize the base.
4. 1.0 M.
5. 100.1 g.
6. Answers will vary. Baking soda is normally a source of base.
7. It increases as the solution becomes more basic.

Student Activity Workbook

● H-5-1: STUDY GUIDE

1. ionization	14. oxygen
2. superscript	15. 12
3. hydroxide	16. molarity
4. Acids	17. protein
5. sour	18. 7
6. blue	19. carbon dioxide
7. slippery	20. buffer
8. relative	21. high
9. neutral	22. botulism
10. acid	23. basic
11. base	24. acidic
12. titration	25. bacteria
13. periodic table	

● H-5-2: CODED MESSAGES

1. titration	7. indicator
2. atomic mass	8. equivalence point
3. buffer	9. molarity
4. neutral	10. a periodic table will tell the atomic number of an element.
5. concentration	
6. mole	

H-5-3: ANALOGIES

1.	a.	9.	b.
2.	a.	10.	c.
3.	c.	11.	c.
4.	b.	12.	c.
5.	c.	13.	d.
6.	d.	14.	c.
7.	c.	15.	15.
8.	d.		

H-5-4: NUTRITION AND YOU

1. carbohydrates
2. gastric juice
3. large intestine
4. neutral
5. small intestine
6. stomach
7. minerals
8. proteins
9. nutrient

The secret word is digestion.

Experiment 5-1: THE pH OF COMMON FOODS

1. All solutions with pH values less than 7.
2. All solutions with pH values greater than 7.
3. Deionized water may be neutral depending on the area (this is the only possibility among the solutions listed).
4. The final pH fell between the pH of the acid and the pH of the base. If the acid and base were mixed in exactly the correct proportions, the pH would be 7. Neutralization.
5. A gas was given off. Used in baking to make doughs and batters rise.
6. No, the pH of tap water varies with the location because solids and gases dissolved in it affect pH.

Experiment 5-2: NEUTRALIZATION

1. Yes, all brands of vinegar contain approximately the same amount.
2. Cider or wine vinegar—they contain other, less harsh flavors in addition to acetic acid.
3. It doesn't really matter, since they all contain the same concentration of acetic acid.

Teacher's Resource Guide

Experiment 5-A: USING RED CABBAGE TO IDENTIFY ACIDS AND BASES

1. Red in acid; green or blue in base.
2. Answers will vary depending on how unknowns are labeled.
3. If the color remains red, the acid was stronger. If the color stays green/blue, the base was stronger. If the color turns purple, they were approximately the same strength.

Experiment 5-B: TEMPERATURE CHANGE AND THE pH OF CARBONATED BEVERAGES

1. It increases.
2. It decreases. This is apparent from the bubbles that leave as the liquid is heated.
3. The pH increases because, as the carbon dioxide level decreases, the acidity of the liquid also decreases.

Understanding Concentration

Concentration is the measure of the amount of a substance in a given unit of volume. If two acid solutions are compared, the one with the most hydrogen ions in the given volume of water is the more concentrated.

EXPERIMENT 5-A
Using Red Cabbage to Identify Acids and Bases

In addition to commercially prepared chemical indicators, there are many plant pigments that change color when they are mixed with acids or bases. In this experiment, you will prepare an indicator from red cabbage, observe its behavior when mixed with known acids and bases, and then use it to discover if two unknown solutions are acidic or basic.

PROCEDURE

1. Place several pieces of red cabbage in a 400–mL beaker. Add just enough tap water to cover the cabbage. Heat the water to boiling. Boil several minutes until the liquid becomes a dark purple color.
2. Place 5 mL of the first solution to be tested in a test tube. Use a medicine dropper to add 10 drops of the cabbage indicator to the test tube.
3. In your data table, record the pH of the solution as determined in **Experiment 5–1: The pH of Common Foods**, and the color the cabbage indicator turns in the solution.
4. Repeat steps 1–2 with the other known solutions listed in the data table.
5. Obtain 5 mL of unknown X and place in a test tube. Add 10 drops of the cabbage indicator to the test tube. In your data table, record the color of the indicator and, if possible, an approximate pH value.
6. Repeat step 5 with unknown Y.
7. Pour the unknown solutions together and note the color of the mixture. If possible, estimate the pH of the mixture. Record this information in your data table.

QUESTIONS

1. What color does the cabbage indicator turn in an acid? In a base?
2. Was unknown X an acid or a base? Unknown Y?
3. Based on the color of the mixture when the two unknowns were combined, which was stronger, unknown X or unknown Y?

SAMPLE DATA TABLE

Solution	pH	Color of Indicator
vinegar		
lemon–lime soda		
tap water		
sodium bicarbonate		
egg white		
unknown X		
unknown Y		
mixed unknowns		

EXPERIMENT 5-B
Temperature Change and the pH of Carbonated Beverages

SAFETY: Place your initials under each appropriate symbol to show the safety precautions you need to remember when performing this experiment.

Carbon dioxide gas dissolves in water to form a weak acid known as carbonic acid. All carbonated beverages are acidic, since the "fizz" in carbonated drinks is produced by dissolved carbon dioxide. In this experiment, you will test the pH of a sample of carbonated beverage at several temperatures to see if temperature affects the acidity of the solution.

PROCEDURE

1. Fill a test tube half–full of a sample of chilled, colorless, carbonated beverage.
2. Use a thermometer to determine the temperature of the liquid and indicator paper to test its pH. Record these findings in your data table.
3. Fill a 250–mL beaker half–full of tap water and determine the temperature of the water. Place the test tube in the beaker. Wait until the temperature of the liquid in the test tube has reached the same temperature as the water. Again, test the pH and record the temperature and pH in your data table.
4. Place the beaker on a heating element on the stove and slowly warm the beverage to 40°C. Record the temperature and pH.
5. Continue heating the beaker and test tube. Take pH readings at 60°C, 80°C, and 100°C. Record the temperature and pH in your data table.

QUESTIONS

1. What happens to the pH as temperature increases?
2. What happens to the level of carbonation as the temperature increases? How do you know?
3. What happens to the pH of soft drinks as they "go flat?"

SAMPLE DATA TABLE

Temperature	pH

TEXT PAGES 98–111

SUGGESTED TIME SCHEDULE

180-day course—8 days.
90-day course—3 days.

STUDENT OBJECTIVES

- Explain the properties of water that make it a polar molecule.
- Describe hydrogen bonds and how they differ from covalent bonds.
- Discuss the differences between hard water and soft water.
- Compare and contrast heat of fusion and heat of vaporization.
- Explain the functions of water in food preparation.
- Name the two general types of water in food.
- Identify the functions of water in the body.

CHAPTER SUMMARY

- Water is a polar molecule because it has a division of electrical charge.
- Water forms hydrogen bonds when a hydrogen atom of one polar molecule is attracted to the negative end of another polar molecule.
- Hard water contains metal ions, which can affect food, laundry, and dishwashing.
- The heat of fusion and the heat of vaporization are involved in the phase changes of water.
- In food preparation, water acts as a solvent and as a medium for heat transfer, colloidal dispersions, and emulsions.
- Free water and bound water are types of water found in food.
- In the body, water functions as a solvent, a transporter of nutrients, a medium for reactions, a reactant, and a temperature regulator.

BACKGROUND INFORMATION

Water is necessary to life. Therefore it is no surprise that this simple compound is important to food scientists. In Chapter 6, students study the structure and physical properties of water, the role water plays in food preparation, and why water is important as a nutrient.

In discussing the properties of water, point out how many are the result of the polar nature of water. For example, ice floats because it is less dense than liquid water. This is not true of most substances—usually the solid state is more dense than the liquid state.

The boiling point of liquid varies with the pressure over the liquid. Boiling points quoted in tables are generally described as Normal or Standard Boiling Points, which are the boiling points of liquids at standard pressure. Standard atmospheric pressure, which is the average atmospheric pressure at sea level on a clear day, is capable of supporting a column of mercury 760 mm high. It is generally listed as 760 mm Hg. Atmospheric pressure decreases as altitude increases, which in turn causes the boiling points of liquids (including water) to decrease.

Teacher's Resource Guide REPRODUCIBLE MATERIALS

T-8:   Functions of Water in the Body
E-6-A: Purifying Water

ACTIVITIES

1. Ask students to locate newspaper or magazine articles on the topic of water and bring copies of the articles to class. Have students give brief oral reports summarizing the content of these articles. There should be a wide diversity of topics (water in the body, water and food safety, water purity, water in other countries, etc.) which will reinforce the importance of water to human beings.

2. Have students read one or both of the following articles: "The Importance of Water," *National Geographic*, August 1980, page 144, or "Apostles of Purity, Mineral Water Buffs Swear by the Stuff," *Smithsonian*, October 1984, pages 104–114. Discuss the article(s) with students, highlighting the qualities of water that make it such an important compound.

3. Invite a guest speaker from the local water district to talk about water sources, water purity, distribution of water, etc.

4. Invite a guest speaker from a local water treatment company to talk about the degree of hardness or softness in local water, the consequences of this hardness or softness, how a water softener works, etc.

5. Show video: "The Quiet Crisis," INDU, 1980 (55 minutes).

6. Have students locate two or three recipes in which water serves different food preparation functions. Discuss these functions and how they are used in a variety of ways in food preparation.

7. Discuss with students the importance of water in the body. Use **T-8: Functions of Water in the Body** to explain how water is used in the body. It is printed in the *Guide* and in the *Student Activity Workbook*.

8. In preparation for **Experiment 6-1: The Boiling Point of Water**, demonstrate the calibration of thermometers in boiling water.

EXTENSION ACTIVITY

Have students conduct **Experiment 6-A: Purifying Water**.

OVERVIEW OF EXPERIMENTS

● *Experiment 6-1:* THE BOILING POINT OF WATER

Time Required

35 minutes

Objective

Students will observe that, regardless of quantity, samples of water under the same atmospheric pressure boil at the same temperature and that water remains at a constant temperature while it boils.

Equipment

- 12 250-mL beakers
- 12 thermometers
- clock or watch with a second hand
- 12 ring stands
- 12 utility clamps
- 12 1-hole stoppers

Supplies

- graph paper

Helpful Hints

- Before doing this experiment, it is helpful to calibrate the precision of the thermometers to be used. Place the thermometers in one beaker of boiling water. In most cases, there will be some variation in readings. Thermometers can be labeled with -1, -2, +1, +2, etc., to indicate how much they tend to be high or low when used at temperatures near 100°C. Whether the thermometers are labeled or not, students should be made aware that such deviations do occur, since thermometer error must always be taken into consideration during candy making.
- Remind students how to set up a ring stand and utility clamp to support a thermometer held in a one-hole rubber stopper.
- Have half the class use 100 mL water and the other half 200 mL.

Laboratory Simplification

Take reading in step 2 every minute (60 sec.).

Laboratory Enrichment

During the experiment, heat a large kettle of water to boiling. Take the temperature of the water to reinforce the concept that all samples of pure water boil at the same temperature, regardless of the amount.

Expected Data

Depending on the amount of water and the heat setting, the temperature will increase at various rates until the water begins to boil. From this point, the temperature will remain constant.

● Experiment 6-2: DISSOLVING SOLIDS IN WATER

Time Required

40 minutes

Objective

Students will observe that different substances dissolve to different extents in room temperature water and that the solubility of substances varies as the temperature of the water increases.

Equipment

- 36 test tubes
- 12 test tube racks
- 12 metric rulers
- 12 10-mL graduated cylinders
- 36 #2 stoppers
- 12 400-mL beakers
- 12 thermometers

Supplies

- sucrose
- sodium chloride
- 60 g potassium nitrate

Helpful Hints

- Use test tubes that are the same size, since comparative height of the solid in the test tubes is being used throughout the experiment. It is also best to use identical rulers to obtain uniform data throughout the class.
- Potassium nitrate can be purchased from any chemical supply company. However, since only a small quantity is needed, it may be possible to obtain some from the science department in your school.

Expected Data

Exact values will vary depending on the shape of the test tubes, etc. However, the sugar should dissolve completely at room temperature and the potassium nitrate in the hot water. The amount of sodium chloride on the bottom of the test tube should not be noticeably different after heating.

Substance	Height of Original Solid	Height of Solid in 20°C H₂0	Height of Solid in 80°C H₂0
Sucrose	3.9 cm	0 cm	0 cm
Sodium chloride	2.5 cm	0.8 cm	0.8 cm
Potassium nitrate	2.1 cm	1.7 cm	0 cm

● Experiment 6-A: PURIFYING WATER

Note: The procedure for this experiment is printed only in the *Teacher's Resource Guide*.

Time Required

15 minutes

Objective

Students will observe the effect of adding chlorine to water containing living organisms.

Equipment

- 24 test tubes
- 12 (or as many as possible) microscopes
- 12 10-mL graduated cylinders
- 12 25-mL graduated cylinders
- 12 microscope slides
- 12 eye droppers
- 1 plastic squeeze bottle

Supplies

- 240 mL pond water
- 120 mL chlorine bleach

Helpful Hints

- Generally, a biology teacher can suggest a suitable source of water that contains living organisms. You or a student can bring a supply of water from this source to class. Check the water before starting the experiment to be sure there are living organisms present in the sample.

- Point out to students that some parasites are not killed by adding bleach to water. Adding bleach is not a safe way to purify water for drinking while hiking or camping, as was once believed. However, the experiment does illustrate, to some extent, the effects of chlorine. It should help students understand why many metropolitan areas and most swimming pools add chlorine to water to ensure its purity.
- To eliminate spilling bleach, dispense it in a plastic squeeze bottle. Only one bottle is needed since students can bring a graduated cylinder to a designated location to obtain the needed bleach.

Expected Data

Organisms seen swimming in the untreated water should be dead in the water treated with bleach.

ANSWER KEY
Student Text

● ANSWERS TO QUESTIONS IN TEXT:

p. 100
Bicarbonate ions are found in temporarily hard water.

p. 103   Approximately 95°F.

p. 104
Free water is easily squeezed out of a food while bound water cannot easily be separated from the food.

p. 107
1. Your body obtains water through the liquids you drink and from chemical reactions that take place in your body.
2. The three functions of water in the human body are to dissolve nutrients, to carry waste materials produced in the cells, and as an essential reactant in many chemical processes.

● CHECK YOUR FACTS

1. The oxygen end.
2. Hydrogen bonding.
3. By boiling it.

4. Liquid water—when water freezes, the hydrogen bonds cause the molecules to spread out, creating a less dense material.
5. 80 calories per gram.
6. Heat of vaporization.
7. No—the boiling point depends on the atmospheric pressure over the water.
8. A transfer medium for heat; a solvent; a medium for colloidal dispersions; a part of emulsions; a major constituent of food.
9. Free water separates from food when sliced, diced, or dried. Bound water can't separate because it is held tightly in the molecules that make up the food.
10. A solvent; a transporter of nutrients and wastes; a medium for chemical reactions; a reactant in chemical processes; a temperature regulator.
11. Take in and put out the same amount of water.

● CRITICAL THINKING AND PROBLEM SOLVING

1. Hot water has more minerals dissolved in it than cold water.
2. The energy is used to separate the molecules of water rather than to speed them up.
3. Each gram of ice at 0°C will absorb 80 calories of heat energy in melting. Each gram of water at 0°C will absorb only 1 calorie for each degree the temperature increases as the water warms up to the temperature of the surroundings.
4. It is lower in Denver than in New York City because Denver's higher altitude causes lower air pressure.
5. The body uses the evaporation of water to cool itself, which means that water is constantly being removed from the body during the fever. Unless the water is replaced, the person will become dehydrated.
6. Hot tea—the solubility of sugar increases as the temperature of the tea increases.

Student Activity Workbook

● H-6-1: STUDY GUIDE

1. It contains one oxygen atom and two hydrogen atoms bonded at a 105° angle.
2. The oxygen end of the molecule is somewhat negative, and the hydrogen end is somewhat positive.

3. An attraction in polar compounds in which the hydrogen end of one molecule is attracted to the negative end of another molecule.
4. Temporarily hard water contains bicarbonate ions which can be removed by boiling. Water with sulfate ions is permanently hard and must undergo special treatment to soften it.
5. Because it takes more energy to break apart the hydrogen bonds in water.
6. The pressure of the air at sea level on a clear day.
7. Stormy weather brings lower air pressure which causes a lower boiling point.
8. The water is heated first and then transfers the heat by conduction and convection to the food.
9. Between 70–90 percent.
10. A solvent dissolves other substances. The substances that dissolve are solutes.
11. The particles in a colloidal dispersion are larger than the particles in a solution.
12. Two immiscible liquids and an emulsifier.
13. The chemical and physical processes occurring within the living cells of the body.
14. Many of the chemical reactions in metabolism occur in water, and water is a reactant in many of the processes.
15. The perspiration pulls heat from the body as it evaporates, thus lowering body temperature.
16. From food and liquid and from chemical reactions that occur in the body.

● H-6-2: CROSSWORD PUZZLE

Across	Down
2. solvent	1. vaporization
4. polar	3. vapor
6. fusion	5. bone
10. electronegative	7. steam
11. eight	8. altitude
14. sublimation	9. hard
17. free	12. temperature
18. essential	13. condenses
19. water	15. immiscible
20. thirsty	16. constant

● H-6-3: NUTRITION AND YOU

1. many functions
2. transports them to individual cells in your body
3. Chemical and physical processes occurring within the living cells of the body
4. essential

5. perspire
6. exercise, fever
7. The perspiration evaporates off your skin. Energy is required for evaporation to occur and you are the nearest source of energy. The water removes energy from your body as it evaporates and helps the body maintain a constant temperature.
8. 45–60
9. 1. food and liquids you eat   2. chemical reactions in your body
10. 6 to 8

● T-8: FUNCTIONS OF WATER IN THE BODY

1. dissolves
2. wastes
3. regulates
4. chemical reaction
5. reacts

● Experiment 6-1: THE BOILING POINT OF WATER

1. Yes.
2. Yes.
3. Yes, within a degree or two.
4. Yes—water boils at the same temperature, so differences could have been caused by the thermometers.
5. No.

● Experiment 6-2: DISSOLVING SOLIDS IN WATER

1. The sucrose dissolved to the greatest extent. The potassium nitrate dissolved the least.
2. The sodium chloride.
3. No.
4. If solubility changes, solids become more soluble as temperature increases.

Teacher's Resource Guide

● Experiment 6-A: PURIFYING WATER

1. The bleach killed the organisms present.
2. Answers will vary.

Chapter 6: Water
FUNCTIONS OF WATER IN THE BODY

TEXT PAGES 98~111

DIRECTIONS: Fill in the blanks in each phrase below.

1. _____ **Nutrients**

2. **Transports Nutrients and** _____

3. _____ **Body Temperature**

4. **Serves as a Medium for** _____ _____

5. _____ **During Chemical Processes**

6. **WATER: THE** _____ **NUTRIENT**

EXPERIMENT 6-A
Purifying Water

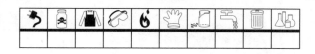

In many parts of the United States, chlorine is added to water to make the water safe to drink. In this experiment, you will observe the effect of chlorine on living organisms found in pond water. The source of chlorine will be household bleach.

PROCEDURE

1. Obtain 20 mL pond water in a 25 mL–graduated cylinder. Pour 10 mL pond water into one test tube and 10 mL into a second test tube.
2. Add 10 mL chlorine bleach to one of the test tubes. Stopper the test tube and shake well.
3. With an eye dropper, place a few drops of the untreated water on a microscope slide and observe it under the microscope. Record your observations in your data table.
4. Thoroughly wash the eye dropper and slide. Place a few drops of the treated water on the slide and observe it under the microscope. Record your observations in your data table.

SAMPLE DATA TABLE

Sample	Appearance
Untreated water	
Treated water	

QUESTIONS

1. What affect did the chlorine bleach have on the organisms present?
2. Does your local water supply contain chlorine? (You may need to contact your local water district to be certain.)

CHAPTER
7
Carbohydrates

TEXT PAGES 112–130

SUGGESTED TIME SCHEDULE

180-day course—10 days.
90-day course—5 days.

STUDENT OBJECTIVES

- Explain the chemical reaction that occurs when plants produce carbohydrates.
- Define monosaccharides and disaccharides and name examples of each.
- Describe the normal regulation of glucose level in the blood and the conditions of low and high glucose levels.
- Explain sugar hydrolysis and list the products of the hydrolysis of sucrose and lactose.
- Discuss the process of caramelization.
- Compare the structures of amylose and amylopectin and how these structures affect cooking properties.
- Define the terms *gelatinization*, *paste*, *retrogradation*, and *syneresis* as used in starch cookery.

CHAPTER SUMMARY

- Carbohydrates, which include sugars, starches, and fibers, are an important part of people's diets all over the world.
- Carbohydrates are formed in green plants through the process of photosynthesis.
- Glucose is the basic sugar unit around which all other carbohydrates are formed.
- The body regulates the amount of glucose in the blood through the hormone insulin.
- Important chemical reactions in the study of sugar include hydrolysis, solubility, and caramelization.
- The size of crystals formed from a sugar solution are affected by temperature, the number of particles,

the rate of crystal growth, interfering agents, and agitation.
- Starches are polysaccharides, which can have either linear or branched structures.
- Starch cookery is based on the gelatinization of starch molecules and the properties of the pastes that are formed.

BACKGROUND INFORMATION

Carbohydrates are the most abundant organic molecules on earth, as well as being the main source of energy for human beings. Chapter 7 presents students with information on the properties of sugars, starches, and fiber, their chemical behavior, and their roles in the body and in food preparation.

The sugar substitutes that are widely used today are complex alcohols or amino acids. They are not digested and used by the body in the same manner as sugars.

Starches can cause tooth decay just as easily as sugars because the amylase enzyme found in saliva starts digesting starches in the mouth. Amylose is broken down into simpler sugars while the food in which it is found is being chewed.

Teacher's Resource Guide
REPRODUCIBLE MATERIALS

T-9:   The Structure of Carbohydrates
Line Spread Test Sheet

ACTIVITIES

1. Have students take and discuss the "Sugar Quiz," *Tufts University Diet and Nutrition Newsletter*, December 1986. How much do students know about sugar?

2. Use **T-9: The Structure of Carbohydrates** to illustrate what the structure of a single sugar looks like, how single sugars join together to form disaccharides, and how they chain to form polysaccharides. This is printed in the *Guide* and in the *Student Activity Workbook*.

3. Have students make and taste test fudge to evaluate the size of the sugar crystals present. How do they think the chocolate and other interfering agents present in the recipe affected crystal size? How did the crystal size of the fudge compare with the size of the crystals in the fondant prepared in **Experiment 7-1: Making Fondant?**

4. Ask students to look at a standard kilocalorie chart and find five foods containing starch and/or fiber that would be suitable for a weight-reducing diet. Have students explain why they chose the foods they did.

5. Invite a person with diabetes (or the parent of a child with diabetes) to discuss the disease, its symptoms, how it has affected eating habits and patterns, how it is controlled, etc.

6. Have students read and discuss the following article: Gregory Cote, "Polysaccharides," *Chem Matters*, April 1986, page 12.

7. Ask each student to bring two food labels to class. Have students identify all the sweetening agents and starches (including gums) listed on the labels. On the chalkboard, make a list of all the sweeteners and starches used. Is the list longer or shorter than students expected? Are any of the products unfamiliar to students?

8. Discuss with students the role carbohydrates play in the body. Why are they an important nutrient?

9. In preparation for **Experiment 7-1: Making Fondant**, demonstrate how to make the control recipe, including how the fondant should be kneaded.

10. In preparation for **Experiment 7-2: Thickening Agents**, demonstrate how to use the line-spread test sheet. This is printed in the *Guide* and in the *Student Activity Workbook*.

OVERVIEW OF EXPERIMENTS

● *Experiment 7-1*: MAKING FONDANT

Time Required

Day 1—45 minutes
Day 2—20 minutes

Objective

Students will observe the effects of various factors on crystal formation.

Equipment

- 1 microscope (5 if available)
- 6 triple beam balances/3 electronic balances
- 12 100-mL graduated cylinders
- 12 saucepans
- 12 candy thermometers
- 12 heat-proof trays
- 12 plastic or wooden spoons
- 12 microscope slides

Supplies

- 2.7 kg sugar
- cream of tartar
- corn syrup
- 0.5 L half-and-half
- plastic wrap
- masking tape
- marking pen
- toothpicks
- glycerol

Helpful Hints

- Be sure to use calibrated thermometers.
- Students will need to look at each other's microscope slides to draw the crystals produced by each variation. If it is possible to borrow five microscopes (one for each variation) from the science department, the process of viewing the slides will be expedited. Students can rotate from one microscope to the next until they have drawn all five sets of crystals. If the science department has a projector microscope you can borrow, you can project each variation on a screen so the whole class can draw the crystals at the same time.
- This experiment is very similar to standard fondant recipes, so it should be fairly easy to carry out successfully.

Laboratory Simplification

Do variations 1 and 4 only.

Laboratory Enrichment

Repeat experiment using a fudge recipe.

Expected Data

Variation Number	Feel of Crystals on Tongue	Texture	Moistness
1	fine	smooth	slight
2	very fine	very smooth	fair
3	very fine	very smooth	fair
4	granular	grainy	dry
5	fine	smooth	moist

● Experiment 7-2: THICKENING AGENTS

Time Required

Day 1—45 minutes
Day 2—25 minutes

Objective

Students will observe the thickening properties of starches to better understand their effect on the final products in which they will be used.

Equipment

- 12 100-mL graduated cylinders
- 12 line-spread sheets
- 12 plastic rings (cylinders) 50.1 mm wide and 25.4 mm high (see below)
- 12 clear pie plates
- 4 muffin tins (depending on size)
- 12 stirring rods
- 24 600-mL glass beakers
- 6 triple beam balances/3 electronic balances
- 12 saucepans
- 24 heat diffusing rings

Supplies

- 1 box baker's paper soufflé cups

- 0.5 kg flour
- 1 package tapioca
- 1 package rice flour
- 1 package potato starch
- 1 package arrowroot
- 1 package corn starch
- masking tape
- marking pen

Helpful Hints

- Buy PVC pipe (used for irrigation) with an outside diameter of 5.3 cm and cut it into 2.5 cm rings. WARNING: PVC is highly toxic, so wear a mask while cutting the rings.
- Because this is a new type of experiment, it is best to demonstrate the entire experiment before the students carry it out. Be sure to stress accuracy in massing as well as safe methods for handling hot beakers containing boiling starch mixtures.
- Show students how to read the line-spread sheets—noting the numbers at four locations, adding the four numbers together, and dividing by 4 to determine the average line spread for the starch.
- It is most convenient to put the soufflé cups of starch to be refrigerated and frozen in muffin tins. Stress that students need to use two paper cups stacked together to provide enough strength to transfer the starch in the paper cups to the labeled muffin tins.
- The number of muffin tins needed depends on the size of the tins and the size of the class. Label the tins with the class period. Half of the tins will be placed in the refrigerator and half in the freezer.
- For best results, thaw the freezer samples for at least 3 hours before they are to be evaluated.

Laboratory Simplification

Perform the lab with three starch samples only.

Laboratory Enrichment

Using a standard recipe, have students bake cherry pies with the starches tested in this experiment. Freeze, thaw, and evaluate the pies. Students could also bake the pies at home as a special assignment. The more unusual thickening agents could be taken home from school to use during preparation of the pies. Family members could evaluate the quality of the pies made at home.

Expected Data

Name of Starch	Amount of Starch	Line-Spread Average		Appearance Refrigerated Sample	Appearance Frozen Sample
		Hot	Cold		
corn	8 g	26	25	runny	runny
corn	16 g	13	11	thick paste	holds shape synersis
rice	8 g	26	26	runny	runny
rice	16 g	16	17	smooth paste	sponge layers, some H_2O loss
tapioca	8 g	25	20	clear	clear
tapioca	16 g	18	15	thick, clear gel	grainy, no synersis
potato	8 g	16	14	jelly fish consistency	holds shape synersis
potato	16 g	10	8	sturdy, holds shape	spongy effect
flour	8 g	24	24	very runny	very runny
flour	16 g	23	23	thin paste soft mound	scalloped, holds shape
arrowroot	8 g	28	23	smooth, soft gel	crystallized synersis
arrowroot	16 g	14	12	thick gel	very firm, holds shape

ANSWER KEY

Student Text

● ANSWERS TO QUESTIONS IN TEXT:

p. 113 Breads, potatoes, and rice.

p. 115
   Maltose in the cereal, lactose in the milk, and sucrose as the table sugar.

p. 125
   1. Cellulose, hemicellulose, and pectin are three fibers made from carbohydrates.

2. Answers will vary, but might include: a sandwich made on whole grain bread with an apple or other fruit for dessert, or a salad made with fresh vegetables, and fruit for dessert.

● CHECK YOUR FACTS

1. Carbon, hydrogen, oxygen.
2. Sugars, starches, fibers.
3. They contain few, if any, of the nutrients needed to maintain a healthy body.
4. Through photosynthesis where green plants convert carbon dioxide, water, and energy from the sun into carbohydrate and oxygen.

5. Monosaccharides are glucose, fructose, and galactose. Disaccharides are sucrose, lactose, and maltose.
6. Fructose.
7. Glucose.
8. Through the hormone insulin and through the action of the kidneys.
9. The enzyme sucrase, heat, acid.
10. Fructose, sucrose, glucose, galactose, maltose, a d lactose.
11. By heating over high temperatures with either a high or low pH.
12. The original concentration of the solution, the presence of particles for the sugar to crystallize on, the temperature of the solution, interfering agents, and agitation.
13. A large molecule formed when small molecules of the same kind join together to form chains.
14. Amylose has a linear structure while amylopectin has a branched structure.
15. The proportion of amylose and amylopectin molecules.
16. The molecules are too large to form a true solution.

● CRITICAL THINKING AND PROBLEM SOLVING

1. Tea with honey—honey contains glucose and fructose which means the body can use the glucose immediately without having to break down a disaccharide first.
2. Fructose, sucrose, and lactose.
3. Yes—a diabetic must watch the entire diet because many foods contain natural sugars or starches that the body breaks down to produce glucose.
4. Temperature controls the concentration of the sugar which is critical to crystal formation, so an accurate thermometer is necessary for successful candy making.
5. The crystals will be large, making the candy a poor quality.
6. Humans don't have the right enzymes to break the bonds in fiber molecules.
7. Caused by using the wrong type of starch or not using enough of it. Prevented by using more starch or a different kind of starch.

Student Activity Workbook

● H-7-1: STUDY GUIDE

1. meat	17. sucrase (invertase)
2. 4	
3. sugar	18. glucose, fructose
4. green plants	19. hydroxyl groups
5. carbohydrate (glucose)	20. caramelization
	21. water
6. glucose	22. sugar solution
7. saccharide	23. supersaturated
8. simple carbohydrate	24. concentration
	25. small
9. hydroxyl	26. interfering
10. Glucose	27. cellulose
11. homeostasis	28. water
12. hormone	29. 10
13. glycogen	30. linear
14. hyperglycemia	31. gelatinization
15. Diabetes	32. retrogradation
16. hydrolysis	33. amylose

● H-7-2: SECRET WORD

1. amylopectin	8. syneresis
2. chlorophyll	9. viscosity
3. sucrose	10. disaccharide
4. paste	11. polymer
5. amylose	12. invert sugar
6. fructose	13. insulin
7. hypoglycemia	14. glucose

The secret word is photosynthesis.

● H-7-3: ANALOGIES

1. a	6. c
2. a	7. a
3. d	8. b
4. c	9. b
5. b	10. b

● H-7-4: NUTRITION AND YOU

1. Cellulose, hemicellulose, and pectin are three fibers made from carbohydrates.
2. Cellulose is the main substance of the cell walls and the woody parts of plants.
3. Humans cannot digest fiber because they do not have the right enzymes to break the bonds in the fiber molecules.

4. Fiber is best known for preventing or relieving constipation.

5. Sources of fiber include fruits, vegetables, nuts, and whole grain breads and cereals.

6. Some nutritionists believe fiber binds with food that has the potential to cause cancer, thereby preventing it from being absorbed into the blood stream.

7. Diabetics are encouraged to eat high-fiber diets to decrease the amouint of insulin their bodies need.

8. The average person in the United States consumes far less fiber than people in other parts of the world (4 g/day vs. 30 g/day).

9. A high-fiber diet is not recommended when a person is recovering from surgery of the stomach or intestines or is suffering from an infection of the lower bowels.

10. Answers will vary, but could include a sandwich made on whole grain bread with fruit for dessert, a salad made with raw vegetables, with nuts and fruits for dessert.

● T-9: THE STRUCTURE OF CARBOHYDRATES

1. fructose
2. sucrose
3. cellulose

● Experiment 7-1: MAKING FONDANT

1. Variations 2 or 3 produced the smallest crystals because the interfering agents present kept the crystals small. Variation 4 produced the largest crystals because of the high temperature during agitation.

2. It began higher than that of pure water and continued to rise as long as it was heated.

3. Either variation 2 or 3 could be used, though variation 3 would probably be best. The low acidity is an advantage because of the chocolate used in making fudge.

● Experiment 7-2: THICKENING AGENTS

1. Answers will vary.
2. **a.** Potato starch **b.** Potato starch **c.** Arrowroot.
3. Most starches firmed up.
4. Most starches lost water and became spongy.
5. Tapioca—it displayed no syneresis, and it was clear. Arrowroot would also be a possibility because it also displayed little syneresis and produced a smooth, clear product.

Chapter 7: Carbohydrates
THE STRUCTURE OF CARBOHYDRATES

TEXT PAGES 112–130

DIRECTIONS: Identify the common name for each molecule shown below.

1. A Monosaccharide: _____

2. A Disaccharide: _____

3. A Polysaccharide: Part of a _____ Molecule

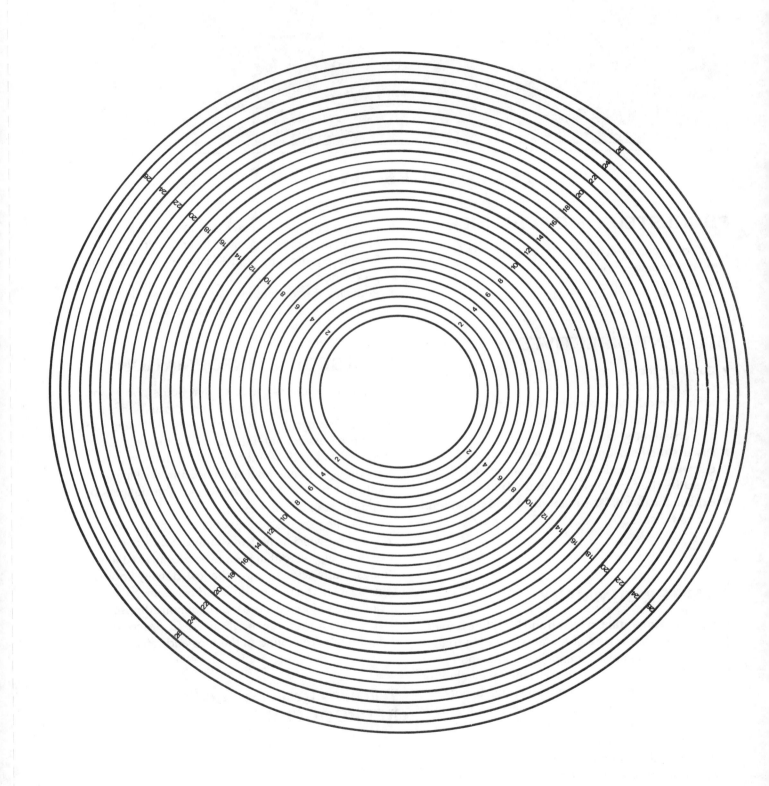

CHAPTER

8

Lipids

TEXT PAGES 131-145

SUGGESTED TIME SCHEDULE

180-day course—8 days.
90-day course—4 days.

STUDENT OBJECTIVES

- Compare the properties of saturated and unsaturated fatty acids.
- Identify foods that contain different types of triglycerides and tell which foods contain saturated and unsaturated fat.
- Discuss the functions of fat in food preparation.
- List ways lipid oxidation can be controlled in food.
- Describe the functions of fat in the body.
- Explain the role of fat, saturated fat, and cholesterol in heart disease.

CHAPTER SUMMARY

- Lipids are important in health and body functioning.
- Fatty acids are a part of all fats, including triglycerides, the fats most commonly found in food.
- Saturated fats contain the maximum number of hydrogen atoms, while unsaturated fats do not contain all the hydrogen they can because of double bonds between carbon atoms.
- In food preparation, fat is used to tenderize, aerate, form emulsions, and add flavor.
- Fat is an important heat medium for sautéing or deep-frying food.
- Fat develops a rancid flavor when it oxidizes, or loses electrons by combining with oxygen.

- In the body, fat regulates temperature, provides energy, promotes healthy skin and hair, provides fat-soluble vitamins, and is needed for hormone production.
- Reducing the amount of total fat, saturated fat, and cholesterol eaten can help prevent heart disease.

BACKGROUND INFORMATION

Chapter 8 explains the roles that lipids play in the body and in food preparation. After a discussion of the properties and composition of lipids, including the difference between saturated and unsaturated fat, the chapter lists the different types of fat that are part of most diets, explains how fat is used in cooking, and points out both the importance and the dangers of including fat in the diet.

Consuming excessive amounts of fish oil, such as cod liver oil, which is high in vitamins A and D, can be toxic. It is suggested that people eat ocean fish high in Omega 3 fatty acids to lower the low-density lipoproteins (LDL) in the blood, but avoid consuming fish oil.

Cellulite is nothing more than common adipose (fat) tissue. The term is generally used to describe the dimpled fat often found in the hips and thighs.

Teacher's Resource Guide
REPRODUCIBLE MATERIALS

T-10:   Formation of a Triglyceride

ACTIVITIES

1. Introduce the topic of lipids to students, discussing how they are formed and the difference between fats and oils and saturated and unsaturated fats. Use **T-10: Formation of a Triglyceride** to help students understand how most of the fats found in food are formed. It is printed in the *Guide* and in the *Student Activity Workbook*.

2. Have students survey margarine labels to determine what oils have been used in the products. How many contain corn or soybean oil? Which are unsaturated fats? How many contain cottonseed or palm oil? Which are saturated fats? Which margarine product(s) would students recommend for people who wanted to reduce their intake of saturated fat?

3. Have students read and discuss one or more of the following articles:
   - Dora J. Hambin, "To Italy, Olive Oil is Green Gold," *Smithsonian*, March 1985, pages 98–109.
   - "Nut Oil in the News," *Sunset Magazine*, January 1982, page 49.
   - "The Greenland Diet," FDA *Consumer*, October 1986, page 6.
   - "Snacks of Pure Vegetable Oils," *Tufts University Diet and Nutrition Newsletter*, May 1987.

4. Demonstrate the differences in melting points among lard, butter, hydrogenated shortening, and margarine. Allow the melted fats to cool, demonstrating the difference between the melting and solidification points of each fat.

5. Have students locate recipes which use fats for each of the five purposes described in the chapter: tenderizing, aeration, a heat medium, in emulsions, and for flavor. What specific fat or oil would they recommend using for each recipe? Why?

6. Invite a dietitian or physician to speak to the class about the latest research on saturated/unsaturated fat, lipoprotein levels, and cholesterol. What implications does this research have for diet and eating patterns?

7. Because **Experiment 8-1: Fat Content of Ground Beef** involves raw meat, be sure students wash their hands before and after the experiment and dispose of their material properly.

8. Because students may not have skill in handling pie crust, demonstrate the techniques needed for **Experiment 8-2: Lipids and Tenderizing**.

OVERVIEW OF EXPERIMENTS

● *Experiment 8-1:* FAT CONTENT OF GROUND BEEF

Time Required

45 minutes

Objective

Students will determine the percent fat (by mass) of several samples of ground beef, and compare their results with the amounts specified on the store labels.

Equipment

- 3 electronic balances
- 12 600-mL beakers
- 12 100-mL beakers
- heat source

Supplies

- 4 0.3-kg (.66 lb) samples of ground beef of different fat contents
- weighing paper

Helpful Hints

- If students have difficulty pouring the fat off of the water in the beaker, they may find it easier to spoon the fat off and place it in the previously massed 100-mL beaker. They should make every effort not to leave any fat in the original beaker or on the spoon.
- A second alternative is to place the beaker containing the fat, water and meat in the refrigerator until the fat congeals on the top, and then to spoon it into the 100-mL beaker for massing.

Laboratory Simplification

None.

Laboratory Enrichment

None.

Expected Data

Masses of beef, fat, and percent of fat will vary.

● *Experiment 8-2*: LIPIDS AND TENDERIZING

Time Required

Day 1—45 minutes
Day 2—20 minutes

Objective

Students will observe the shortening effect of various lipids in pie crust.

Equipment

- 3 electronic balances
- 24 mixing bowls
- 12 100-mL graduated cylinders
- 12 sifters
- 12 pastry blenders
- 12 forks
- 12 rolling pins
- 12 13-cm pie pans
- 12 knives

Supplies

- 2 kg flour
- salt
- hydrogenated shortening
- lard
- margarine
- vegetable oil

Helpful Hints

- Have all ingredients at room temperature before the experiment.
- Use only fresh lard because lard turns rancid easily. Rancidity will affect the experimental results.
- Small disposable pie pans are recommended for this experiment. The control recipe is not designed for a standard 23-cm pie pan.
- If you prefer, students could prepare and bake the pie crusts on Day 1. The crusts could then be filled with a cream filling before the evaluation on Day 2 of the experiment.

Laboratory Simplification

Have students perform fewer variations.

Laboratory Enrichment

None.

Expected Data

Variation	Texture	Tenderness	Flavor
1	layered	tender	excellent
2	crumbly	very tender	slightly unpleasant
3	layered	less tender	excellent
4	oily	less tender	too oily

ANSWER KEY

Student Text

● ANSWERS TO QUESTIONS IN TEXT:

p. 135
Hydrogenated oils stay fresh longer.

p. 136
Three commercially important animal fats are butter, lard, and beef.

p. 137
Water will cause the fat to spatter and the spattering fat can burn the person frying.

p. 138
To prevent food from becoming rancid.

p. 141
Fish that contain high levels of Omega 3 fatty acids are sardines, salmon, tuna, and herring.

CHECK YOUR FACTS

1. A carbon chain to which hydrogen atoms are attached with a carboxyl group at one end.
2. -COOH. Organic acids.
3. A major type of food lipid. By the reaction of alcohol with fatty acids.
4. Those that contain oleic and/or linoleic acids.
5. They reduce the chances of heart disease, and they are high in vitamins A and D.
6. Butter, lard, and beef fat.
7. They aerate the batter by forming bubbles around gas pockets. This makes the cake lighter.
8. Butter, bacon fat, and olive oil.
9. Linolenic acid.
10. To minimize oxidation, which can cause rancid flavors.
11. Maintains body temperature, helps protect vital organs, provides energy, maintains health of skin and hair, and is needed for hormone production.
12. They contain Omega 3 fatty acids, which make it more difficult for plaque to form and make plaque less sticky, so it is less apt to collect in the arteries.

● CRITICAL THINKING AND PROBLEM SOLVING

1. Saturated fats contain only single bonds between carbon atoms which make them chemically more stable and more difficult to break down than unsaturated fats, which contain double bonds between some of the carbon atoms.
2. Hydrogen is added to unsaturated fats, which are usually oils, transforming them into saturated fats, which are usually semisolid.
3. The solidification point is lower than the melting point.
4. Lard will add more flavor than vegetable oil, but, as a saturated fat, it is more of a health risk than vegetable oil, an unsaturated fat.
5. The heavy use it gets causes it to break down or crack.
6. They increase it.
7. Answers will vary.
8. Answers will vary.

Student Activity Workbook

● H-8-1: STUDY GUIDE

1. Lipids.
2. Organic solvents.
3. Organic compounds made of a carbon chain to which hydrogen atoms are attached with a carboxyl group at one end.
4. Acetic acid—a two-carbon chain.
5. A covalent bond in which each atom donates one electron to form the bond.
6. A fat in which all bonds between carbon atoms are single.
7. A fat molecule that does not contain all the hydrogen it could contain.
8. A fat is usually a saturated compound that is solid at room temperature while an oil is usually an unsaturated compound that is liquid at room temperature.
9. The temperature at which melted fat regains its original firmness.
10. Milk fat, coconut palm fat, vegetable butter, oleic or linoleic acids, linolenic acid, animal fat, and marine oil.
11. The fatty tissue of a hog.
12. Tenderizing, aeration, a heat medium, in emulsions, and as a flavoring.
13. The breakdown of fat from repeated heating.
14. It is well insulated, has high sides, and a reliable thermostat.
15. The water in a wet food will cause spattering that may burn the person who is frying.
16. A chemical change in which a substance loses electrons. Usually it occurs when the substance combines with oxygen.
17. Adipose tissue.
18. Linoleic and linolenic acids.
19. Fat provides 9 kcal per gram while carbohydrates provide only 4 kcal per gram.
20. Limiting the kilocalories from fat to less than 30 percent of the total kilocalories consumed.
21. In the liver.
22. Cholesterol and other fats.
23. A low risk of heart disease.

H-8-2: SCRAMBLED WORDS

1. hydrogenation
2. solidification
3. lipids
4. cholesterol
5. cracking
6. marine
7. saturated
8. margarine
9. linoleic
10. plaque
11. rancid
12. animal
13. sunflower
14. tenderize
15. oxidation

H-8-3: ANALOGIES

1. d
2. c
3. b
4. b
5. d
6. c
7. d
8. b
9. a
10. b

H-8-4: CROSSWORD PUZZLE

Across
3. triglycerides
5. oxidation
7. adipose tissue
10. hydrogenation
12. lipids
13. saturated fat
14. double bond

Down
1. cholesterol
2. plaque
4. rancid
6. fatty acids
8. lipoproteins
9. unsaturated fat
11. single bond

H-8-5: NUTRITION AND YOU

1. Make it more difficult for the plaque to form or clump together and make plaque less sticky and less likely to collect on the arteries.
2. sardines, salmon, tuna, herring . . .
3. Cod stores its Omega 3 fatty acids in its liver.
4. Choose lean meats, poultry, fish and dried beans. Use skim milk and skim milk cheeses. Eat liver and eggs only occasionally. Limit the butter, cream, lard, and shortening you eat. Trim excess fat from your meat. Bake, boil, and broil foods instead of frying. Read labels to discover the amounts and kinds of fats in foods.
5. It helps you know your possible risk of heart disease.

T-10: FORMATION OF A TRIGLYCERIDE

1. glycerol
2. fatty acid
3. triglyceride

Experiment 8-1: FAT CONTENT OF GROUND BEEF

1. Heat liquifies the fat, making it easier to separate.
2. Answers will vary.
3. Answers will vary, but usually the lower the fat content, the higher the price per pound.
4. Answers will vary, but will probably be lower than the label values.
5. Answers will vary, but generally student values are lower than the label values because it is very difficult to recover all the fat floating on the water in step 5. In addition, stores may legally sell meat with a lower fat content than what is printed on the label; they simply may not exceed that limit.

Experiment 8-2: LIPIDS AND TENDERIZING

1. The one made with lard.
2. The one made with hydrogenated shortening.
3. Both variations 1 (hydrogenated shortening) and 3 (margarine) were excellent.
4. No, because pies and cakes have different consistencies.

Chapter 8: Lipids

FORMATION OF A TRIGLYCERIDE

TEXT PAGES 131–145

DIRECTIONS: A triglyceride is formed when 3 fatty acid molecules become attached to glycerol in place of the hydrogens of the hydroxyl groups. "R" is a shorthand way of referring to the rest of the compound. Identify each lipid compound below.

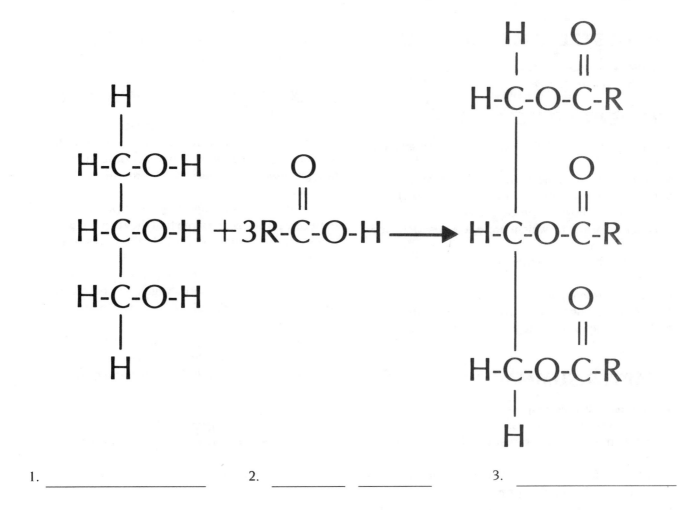

1. _____   2. _____ _____   3. _____

CHAPTER
9
Protein

TEXT PAGES 146-159

SUGGESTED TIME SCHEDULE

180-day course—9 days.
90-day course—3 days.

STUDENT OBJECTIVES

- Name the groups of elements that identify an amino acid.
- Describe the chemical structure of protein.
- Explain what happens during the denaturation of protein and how the process occurs.
- Describe ways in which protein is used in food preparation.
- Discuss the composition of eggs and how they should be stored.
- List factors that affect the stability of an egg foam.
- Identify the functions of protein in the body.
- Compare and contrast complete and incomplete protein.

CHAPTER SUMMARY

- Proteins are made up of chains of amino acids joined by peptide bonds.
- Protein molecules are denatured by heat and other factors.
- Protein is found in a variety of foods and reacts in many ways during food preparation.
- Eggs are a nutritious food, which need proper storage to retain their quality.
- Foam formation depends on the temperature, pH, and quality of the egg; the type of beating; and the presence of other substances.
- In the body, food protein is used for building and repairing tissues, making proteins that regulate body processes, maintaining pH, and providing energy.

- Complete proteins are needed in the diet to provide the eight essential amino acids.

BACKGROUND INFORMATION

In Chapter 10, students study the structure and function of protein to understand why protein is nutritionally important to human beings. In addition, the techniques needed for successful protein cookery are introduced.

Protein molecules are huge compared to other molecules. They are so large that they cannot form true solutions, but rather form colloidal dispersions, both in the body and in foods, such as milk.

Protein molecules are unique because they are formed by peptide bonds, which are normally very weak. A denatured protein is one in which the peptide bond has unfolded. This process is sometimes reversible. However, if it continues until coagulation occurs, it is irreversible. A familiar example of denaturation/coagulation is a clear egg white turning white and opaque.

Teacher's Resource Guide
REPRODUCIBLE MATERIALS

T-11:   The Effects of Heat on Meat

ACTIVITIES

1. Discuss with students the chemical nature of protein. Peptide bonds in amino acid chains and the denaturation process are unique to protein. Discuss the factors that cause peptide bonds to

unfold, e.g., heat, acid, freezing, enzymes, agitation, irradiation, sound waves, pressure, salt, etc.

2. Have students sample seviche or pickled herring and discuss how the protein is denatured in these products (by acid rather than heat.) OR Demonstrate how to make seviche and have students monitor how the acid denatures the protein.

3. Discuss the structure of eggs and show eggs of different qualities. Quality can be related to grade or to length of time the eggs have been stored. Review proper storage techniques.

4. Have students read and discuss one or both of the following articles: "Eggs and Cholesterol," *University of California at Berkeley Wellness Newsletter*, May 1987, page 8 or Arthur E. Grosser, "Eggs, the Inside Story," *Chem Matters*, December 1984, page 4.

5. Use "The Incredible Edible Egg" or other information from the Egg Action Council as reference or resource material. Write: Egg Action Council/ National Egg Network, 729 8th St., S.E., Washington, D.C. 20003. 1-800-342-2437 or 1-202-547-3101.

6. Discuss the principles of protein cookery. Use **T-11: The Effects of Heat on Meat** to highlight what happens as the temperature rises during meat cookery. This is printed in the *Guide* only.

7. Discuss with students the role of protein in the body. Review the protein RDA and help students determine whether they are getting enough protein in their diets.

8. Review complete and incomplete proteins and the implications for planning vegetarian diets. Have students plan a week-long vegetarian menu that would provide all the essential amino acids. They could use the Four Food Group Plan for Vegetarians as a reference.

9. In preparation for **Experiment 9-1: Egg Foam Stability**, demonstrate how to prepare an egg foam, showing students what the foam looks like at each stage—foamy, soft peaks, stiff peaks, and overbeaten. Demonstrate how to set up the funnel in the graduated cylinder to test for leakage.

OVERVIEW OF EXPERIMENTS

● *Experiment* 9-1: EGG FOAM STABILITY

Time Required

45 minutes

Objective

Students will observe differences in the quality of egg foam after adding sugar at various points in the beating process.

Equipment

- 6 triple beam balances/3 electronic balances
- 24 containers in which to separate eggs
- 12 beaters
- 12 equal-sized mixing bowls
- 12 150-mL beakers
- 12 100-mL graduated cylinders
- 12 funnels
- 12 metric rulers
- clock or watch with second hand

Supplies

- sugar
- 24 large eggs

Helpful Hints

- Eggs should be at room temperature when students begin this experiment.
- If you prefer, students can use graduated cylinders to measure the sugar. Students will need 30 mL sugar if this method is used.
- Students need to be reminded to handle the foam gently to avoid breaking the air pockets in the foam when putting it in the funnel.
- Draw a data table on the chalkboard and have students report their results on the chalkboard as well as in their data tables. The results from all the variations are needed to complete the experiment questions.

Laboratory Simplification

Do variations 1 and 5.

Laboratory Enrichment

Have students bake lemon meringue pies using the foams produced during this experiment. They can evaluate the quality of the meringues made with each experiment variation.

Expected Data

Variation	Time Before Adding Sugar	Time After Adding Sugar	Total Beating Time	Height in cm	Leakage in mL
1	—	5.5 min.	5.5 min.	1.5	5 drops
2	.5 min.	4.5 min.	5 min.	1.5	2 drops
3	1.5 min.	3 min.	4.5 min.	1.75	none
4	2 min.	1.5 min.	3.5 min.	1.75	none
5	—	—	2 min.	2	none

● Experiment 9-2: THE EFFECT OF ACID ON PROTEIN

Time Required

30 minutes

Objective

Students will compare the behavior of egg white in pure water and in vinegar to observe how acid affects protein.

Equipment

- 1 400-mL beaker
- 24 150-mL beakers
- 12 metal teaspoons
- 24 large saucepans

Supplies

- 1 bottle white vinegar
- 4–6 egg whites (depending on size)

Helpful Hints

- Separate the eggs ahead of time, putting the egg whites in the 400-mL beaker. Students can take the amount of egg white they need from the beaker.
- Be sure to review the procedure used in this experiment, so that in step 5 students will understand that they are to stir the water in the saucepan, not the water in the beaker.

Laboratory Simplification

None.

Laboratory Enrichment

Substitute egg yolk or fish instead of egg white, and check the temperature difference needed for coagulation.

Expected Data

The egg white in water will be stringy—almost like a spider web. The egg white in acid will form a smooth cohesive mass.

ANSWER KEY

Student Text

● ANSWERS TO QUESTIONS IN TEXT:

p. 147
Enzymes are the proteins that control chemical activity in living organisms.

p. 149
Fibrous proteins are made of ropelike fibers shaped like a coiled metal spring, while globular proteins are shaped more like a ball of steel wool and are not as strong as fibrous proteins.

p. 151
Egg albumin coagulates at 56°C.

p. 154
Infants require nine amino acids.

p. 155   48 g of protein.

1. Red blood cells must be replaced every three or four months.
2. It is important that proteins are amphoteric because one role they play is helping body systems maintain stable pH levels.

● CHECK YOUR FACTS

1. They are large molecules made up of many amino acids.
2. A carboxyl group is -COOH and an amine group is -NH₂.
3. One of the hydrogen atoms attached to the nitrogen atom in the amine group comes off and a second amino acid attaches to the first one.
4. Collagen, myosin, keratin, and elastin.
5. Heat, freezing, sound waves, irradiation, and beating or whipping.
6. Sodium and potassium ions.
7. When coagulation has not occurred.
8. The shell, inner and outer shell membranes, egg white, chalaza, and egg yolk.
9. Amount of air incorporated, freshness of the egg, pH, type and time of beating, temperature, and the presence of other substances.
10. It is needed to build and repair body tissues.
11. The body can manufacture the others.
12. Grains and seeds, such as rice and beans or wheat and soy.

● CRITICAL THINKING AND PROBLEM SOLVING

1. The protein molecules uncoil (denature) before they can collide with other protein molecules and clump together to form a solid (coagulate).
2. One end of the molecule found in egg yolk dissolves in oil, while the other end dissolves in water. As a result, the egg yolk can stabilize the oil-in-water mixture.
3. If the protein in the flour is not fully coagulated (not solidified), the bread may collapse because the shock makes the gas bubbles leave the bread suddenly, which causes the bread to fall.
4. Because chickens can manufacture vitamin C in their bodies.
5. Carbon dioxide escapes through the egg shell, causing the albumin to become more basic, thus increasing pH.

6. Because it is better to store them covered.
7. No—the eggs need to be at room temperature and the sugar should be added at the end to produce the best foam.
8. They lack the amino acids needed to produce the protein that promotes healing.
9. Answers will vary.

Student Activity Workbook

● H-9-1: STUDY GUIDE

1. Structural protein, protein that controls body processes, and food protein.
2. It is digestible, nontoxic, and available for human consumption.
3. Hydrogen, carbon, oxygen, nitrogen, and sometimes other elements.
4. A type of organic acid found in protein.
5. A protein molecule containing many peptide bonds.
6. The order of the amino acids connected by the peptide bonds.
7. It changes the shape of a protein molecule without breaking its covalent bonds.
8. Heat.
9. A product formed when a liquid is whipped, trapping air in the liquid.
10. An elastic, stretchy protein found in wheat that gives baked goods structure.
11. The albumin.
12. Iron, phosphorus, vitamin A, thiamin, and riboflavin.
13. The white becomes less viscous and more watery, and the yolk becomes more watery and thinner.
14. After the egg whites have been beaten until foamy.
15. Vinegar.
16. Enzymes and hormones.
17. They help maintain a stable pH level because they can act as either an acid or a base.
18. Methionine, threonene, tryptophan, isoleucine, leucine, lysine, valine, phenylalanine.
19. Complete protein contains all eight essential amino acids while incomplete protein lacks one or more of the essential amino acids.
20. The person's stage of development.

H-9-2: CROSSWORD PUZZLE

Across
3. peptide
5. coagulation
8. amine
10. hormones
12. chalaza
15. amino
16. enzymes
17. irradiation
18. incomplete

Down
1. macromolecules
2. egg
4. denaturation
6. actin
7. antibodies
9. collagen
10. hemoglobin
11. foams
13. amphoteric
14. albumin
19. pH

H-9-3: ANALOGIES

1. b
2. d
3. d
4. a
5. c
6. c
7. b
8. b
9. b
10. d
11. c
12. b
13. c
14. c
15. b

H-9-4: NUTRITION AND YOU

1. People of all ages need protein to build body tissue and replace worn-out cells.
2. Your body constantly needs new hair and nail cells, replacement cells in the intestinal tract, and replacement red blood cells.
3. Red blood cells are replaced every three or four months.
4. Enzymes and hormones are proteins that control body processes.
5. Your body needs food protein in order to build other proteins.
6. Antibodies are a form of protein that help the body fight disease.
7. Lypoproteins transport lipids in the blood.
8. Proteins can be used as a source of energy if your body has an insufficient supply of carbohydrate or fat, or if you eat more protein than your body needs.
9. It is important that proteins are amphoteric because one of their functions is to help body systems maintain stable pH levels.
10. Answers will vary but may include milk products, eggs, meat, and fish.

Experiment 9-1: EGG FOAM STABILITY

1. The egg white beaten without any sugar added to it.
2. The sample to which the sugar was added first (variation 1).
3. Variation 1.
4. After the egg whites have been beaten.

Experiment 9-2: THE EFFECT OF ACID ON PROTEIN

1. The beaker with the vinegar.
2. The acid affected how the egg coagulated, causing the egg to hold together better.
3. Vinegar—the egg holds together better causing a firmer, less stringy product.
4. Other acids, such as lemon juice, or table salt.

The Effects of Heat on Meat

Temperature °C	Color of Meat	Fibrous Proteins (Myosin & Actin)	Protein–bound Water	Connective Tissue (Collagen & Elastin)
38	red	uncoil begin to coagulate	begin to flow	
60	pink			begins to dissolve
71		mostly coagulated		
82	gray–brown	form a denser association	flow ceases	
93				dissolves rapidly

CHAPTER 10

Vitamins and Minerals

TEXT PAGES 160-175

SUGGESTED TIME SCHEDULE

180-day course—8 days.
90-day course—4 days.

STUDENT OBJECTIVES

- Describe water- and fat-soluble vitamins and list the main vitamins in each category.
- Explain why megadoses of fat-soluble vitamins can be toxic.
- Discuss the functions of vitamins and minerals in the body.
- Describe food sources for the various vitamins and minerals.
- Identify deficiency diseases and explain their causes.
- Distinguish between major and trace minerals and list examples in each category.
- Identify some interrelationships among nutrients.

CHAPTER SUMMARY

- Vitamins and minerals perform specific functions in the body that are vital to life.
- Deficiency diseases resulting from a lack of vitamins or minerals are beriberi, pellagra, rickets, osteomalacia, scurvy, osteoporosis, and anemia.
- Different foods are good sources of different vitamins and minerals, so it is important to eat a variety of foods to get your Recommended Dietary Allowances of each.
- Water-soluble vitamins dissolve in water, are not stored in the body, and must be eaten every day.
- Fat-soluble vitamins dissolve in lipids, are stored in the body, and can be toxic if taken in megadoses.
- Major minerals are needed in larger amounts in the body than trace minerals.

- Vitamins and minerals interact in body processes, so a deficiency of one affects the functioning of others.

BACKGROUND INFORMATION

Chapter 10 presents information on the properties and functions of selected water- and fat-soluble vitamins. The roles of major and trace minerals in the body are also discussed. The interaction of vitamins and minerals as well as other nutrients is highlighted.

The importance of vitamins and minerals in the diet is constantly stressed in the mass media. A wide variety of foods have nutrients added during processing, such as milk fortified with vitamin D and orange juice with added calcium.

Students should understand that vitamins and minerals are needed by the body in minute quantities. Larger amounts are useless for good health and, in fact, can be toxic if taken in excessive quantities. This is especially true of the fat-soluble vitamins—A, D, and E. Unless a physician has prescribed megadoses of vitamins for therapeutic reasons, students should not take more than the recommended allowances.

The word calcium comes from the Latin word, "clox," which means chalk. It was apparently given this name because many of its compounds are powder-like chalky substances.

Teacher's Resource Guide
REPRODUCIBLE MATERIALS

T-12: Nutrient Interaction

ACTIVITIES

1. Display a variety of vitamin and/or mineral pills. Why do people take pills such as these? How do people know how much to take? What happens if someone takes too many vitamin pills? What are the advantages and disadvantages of having candy-flavored vitamin pills for children?

2. Ask students to locate articles related to vitamins or minerals in newspapers or magazines and bring copies of the articles to class. Have students give brief oral reports summarizing the content of these articles. Do students believe the information presented in these articles? How can they evaluate the information presented?

3. Discuss with students the various water- and fat-soluble vitamins. Review the effects of heat, light, pH, and other factors on the stability of vitamins.

4. Show the film: "Vitamins from Food," PERE, 1978 (20 minutes) or another film on the importance of vitamins in the diet.

5. Have students read and discuss the following article: "Medical Makeover," *Ladies Home Journal*, July 1986, page 30. Have students distinguish between what the article actually says and what it implies is true. Also have them consider how some parts of the article could be misunderstood.

6. Discuss with students the interaction of nutrients. Use **T-12: Nutrient Interaction** to visually illustrate the interaction among vitamin D, calcium, and phosphorus. This is printed in the *Guide* and in the *Student Activity Workbook*. Have students draw diagrams illustrating other nutrient interactions.

7. In preparation for **Experiment 10-1: Titration of Vitamin C**, demonstrate the procedure used. Explain the calculations that will be used to determine the amount of vitamin C in each sample.

OVERVIEW OF EXPERIMENTS

● Experiment 10-1: TITRATION OF VITAMIN C

Time Required

45 minutes

Objective

Students will determine the effect of heat on vitamin C by titrating heated and unheated samples of apple and orange juice.

Equipment

- 12 100-mL graduated cylinders
- 12–24 50-mL burets
- 12 ring stands
- 12 utility clamps
- 12 250-mL Erlenmeyer flasks

Supplies

- 1 340-g can frozen apple juice (vitamin C added)
- 1 340-g can frozen orange juice
- 600 mL oxalic acid solution (see below)
- 100 mL 2.6 dichloroindophenol solution (see below)
- 100 mL ascorbic acid solution (see below)
- deionized or distilled water

Helpful Hints

- The oxalic acid solution is prepared by adding 12 g oxalic acid to enough deionized or distilled water to make 600 mL solution. Caution: When mixing the oxalic acid, use a fume hood; wear proper safety clothing, eye guards, and gloves.

- Students should dispense this from a buret to get as accurate an amount as possible. If two burets per laboratory group are not available, students could go to three or four centrally located burets to get the oxalic acid solution.

- The 2.6 dichloroindophenol solution is prepared by adding 0.5 g of the indicator to 1000 mL deionized or distilled water. The indicator is blue in basic solutions and pink in acid solutions.

- The standard ascorbic acid solution is prepared by dissolving 0.02 g ascorbic acid (from a recently opened container) in 100 mL deionized or distilled water.

- As with all titrations, it is best to have students carry out the titration three times and then average the results.

- It is helpful to review titration techniques with students. This can be done while standardizing the oxalic acid solution with standard ascorbic acid solution in the following manner. Add exactly 5 mL standardized ascorbic acid solution to 20 mL oxalic acid solution in a 250-mL Erlenmeyer flask. Titrate this with the dye solution students will use in their experiment until a pink color appears that does not disappear when the flask is swirled. This titration should be repeated at least three times and an average value calculated. Depending on the number of classes you teach, you can do one titration per class and as many extra trials as needed to get at least three values for averaging. This average is used in the equation in step 8 of the experiment.

- Prepare the juices the day before the experiment and have them available for students to use on the day of the experiment.

Laboratory Simplification

None.

Expected Data

Results will vary depending on the brands of juice used and titrating technique. In general, the apple juice contains less vitamin C than the orange juice, and the heated orange juice contains less vitamin C than the refrigerated orange juice.

Variation	Average Class Buret Readings			Mg. Vit C in 100 mL Juice
	Initial	Final	Difference	
1	45 mL	15 mL	30 mL	30 mg
2	40 mL	20 mL	20 mL	20 mg
3	22 mL	20 mL	2 mL	2 mg
4	28 mL	26 mL	2 mL	2 mg

Laboratory Enrichment

Repeat **Experiment 10-1: Titration of Vitamin C** with storage temperature as the variable. Wrap juice containers in foil to exclude light. Store half of each type of juice at room temperature and half in the refrigerator for three to four days before titrating.

Repeat **Experiment 10-1: Titration of Vitamin C** with exposure to light as the variable. Place half the juice in containers wrapped in foil while the rest of the juice is in clear containers. Store the juice at room temperature for three to four days before titrating.

• Experiment 10-2: CALCIUM IN MILK

Time Required

25 minutes

Objective

Students will observe the effects of calcium on the coagulation of milk.

Equipment

- 12 400-mL beakers
- 36 test tubes
- 36 #2 stoppers
- 12 laboratory thermometers
- 3–4 dropping bottles or medicine droppers

Supplies

- 1 L whole milk
- rennet
- sodium citrate
- calcium chloride solution (see below)

Helpful Hints

- The calcium chloride solution is prepared by adding 2 g calcium chloride to 200 mL water. Since so little of this chemical is needed, you may be able to obtain what you need from the chemistry department.

- The calcium chloride solution is placed in three or four dropping bottles from which students can get the small amount of the solution they need. If dropping bottles are not available, place three or four medicine droppers in a small beaker of solution for students to use in dispensing the solution needed.

Expected Data

Test Tube	Appearance After 5 Minutes	Appearance After 10 Minutes
A	milk coagulates	more coagulation
B	no coagulation	coagulation
C	no coagulation	no coagulation

ANSWER KEY
Student Text

● ANSWERS TO QUESTIONS IN TEXT:

p. 161
The RDA of Vitamin C for a 7-year-old female is 45 mg.

p. 163
Provitamins are often called precursors.

p. 165
British sailors became known as limeys because they took limes on long voyages to prevent scurvy.

p. 168
Minerals in which there is a difference between men and women are magnesium and iron. There is a difference in the RDA's due to women's need to build up their blood, due to monthly blood loss.

p. 171
Vitamin C would help your body absorb the iron it needs.

● CHECK YOUR FACTS

1. Complex organic substances vital to life which perform specific functions in the body.

2. Tryptophan.
3. Riboflavin.
4. Niacin.
5. The soda lime used in preparing the corn chemically frees the niacin from the protein in the corn.
6. Vitamin C.
7. Carotene, the precursor of vitamin A.
8. Vitamin D is needed for growth and repair of bones. It helps prevent rickets and osteomalacia.
9. Vitamin K.
10. Major minerals are needed in amounts of 0.1 g or more a day while trace minerals are needed in amounts of 0.01 g or less a day.
11. Excess sodium can cause or aggravate high blood pressure or heart disease.
12. Zinc, selenium, and molybdenum.

● CRITICAL THINKING AND PROBLEM SOLVING

1. They can produce vitamin C in their bodies.
2. A resident of Anchorage—to compensate for not being exposed to the sun as much as a resident of San Diego.
3. Vitamins C and D work with calcium and phosphorus to prevent rickets.
4. The body itself does not make vitamin K, but bacteria that live in the intestines can make it.
5. The antibiotics can kill the bacteria in the intestines that make the vitamin K. If the diet doesn't include enough vitamin K, blood clotting is affected.
6. Orange juice—vitamin C assists the body in absorbing iron. Water would have no impact on iron absorption, while tea would hinder iron absorption.
7. Answers will vary.

Student Activity Workbook

● H-10-1: STUDY GUIDE

1. vitamins
2. vitamin A
3. vitamin B$_{12}$
4. larger
5. deficiency
6. soluble
7. fat-soluble
8. beriberi
9. alcohol
10. vitamin B$_2$
11. light
12. niacin
13. pellagra
14. corn
15. citrus fruits
16. collagen

17. daily
18. megadoses
19. retinol
20. vision
21. liver
22. carotene
23. milk
24. rickets
25. osteomalacia
26. tocopherol
27. major
28. trace
29. sodium
30. Calcium
31. osteoporosis
32. Sulfur
33. iodine

7. Vitamin D
8. Magnesium helps hold the calcium in a tooth's enamel.
9. Selenium
10. calcium

● H-10-2: CROSSWORD PUZZLE

Across
3. scurvy
4. broccoli
6. trace
9. tryptophan
11. acids
13. beriberi
14. corn
15. DNA
16. fat
20. niacin
21. sunshine
24. riboflavin

Down
1. precursor
2. rickets
5. Egypt
7. vitamin
8. water
10. carotene
12. collagen
17. RDA
18. thiamin
19. minerals
22. biotin
23. vision

● T-12: NUTRIENT INTERACTION

1. Vitamin C helps in absorption of iron.
2. Vitamin C interferes with absorption of copper.
3. Tea inhibits the body's ability to absorb iron.
4. Vitamin E helps the body absorb vitamin A.

● Experiment 10-1: TITRATION OF VITAMIN C

1. Information in data table.
2. Yes. The orange juice seemed to lose more of its vitamin C content than the apple juice. However, the apple juice originally contained much less vitamin C.
3. Both should be stored in a refrigerator away from heat.

● H-10-3: NUTRITION AND YOU

1. balance
2. iron and copper
3. up to three times as much
4. anemia
5. Tea inhibits the body's ability to absorb iron.
6. Zinc is a necessary portion of the protein that takes Vitamin A from the liver when it is needed by the body.

● Experiment 10-2: CALCIUM IN MILK

1. The contents of test tube A coagulated due to the rennet. The contents of test tube C were untreated, so remained liquid milk.
2. They combined with the citrate ions to form calcium citrate. This made it impossible for the calcium to coagulate even though rennet was present.
3. There were enough calcium ions present for coagulation to occur.

Chapter 10: Vitamins and Minerals
NUTRIENT INTERACTION

TEXT PAGES 160~175

DIRECTIONS: Calcium, phosphorus, and vitamin D interact to form strong bones. On the lines below, list four other nutrient interactions that are important in the body.

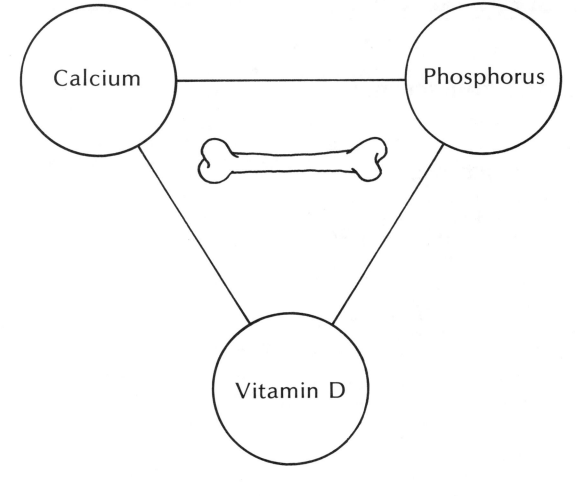

1. _____

2. _____

3. _____

4. _____

CHAPTER 11

Metabolism

TEXT PAGES 176–193

SUGGESTED TIME SCHEDULE

180-day course—9 days.
90-day course—4 days.

STUDENT OBJECTIVES

- Define anabolism and catabolism, the two opposite processes of metabolism.
- Describe conditions needed for metabolism to occur.
- Explain the process of osmosis and the role it plays in metabolism.
- Discuss basal metabolism and factors that affect it.
- Identify various levels of voluntary activity and how these affect the need for kilocalories.
- Describe metabolic changes that can occur during fasting and their effect on the body.
- Explain why lactic acid builds up in the muscles during exercise and how this can be prevented or treated.

CHAPTER SUMMARY

- Energy is needed by the body for metabolism and voluntary activities.
- In metabolism, molecules can be combined or broken down through the processes of anabolism and catabolism.
- Osmosis regulates the concentration of chemicals dissolved in the blood and cells through the movement of fluid through cell membranes.
- Basal metabolism is the amount of energy needed by a body at rest to maintain the automatic activities that support life.

- Basal metabolism is measured by the basal metabolic rate, which uses kilocalories per hour to measure the heat produced by a body at rest after a 12–hour fast.
- Voluntary activities use varying amounts of kilocalories depending on the physical work involved and the time spent.
- Fasting can be dangerous because it disrupts the normal metabolic processes.
- Extreme muscle fatigue during exercise is the result of the buildup of lactic acid because of a lack of enough oxygen to completely break down glucose.

BACKGROUND INFORMATION

In Chapter 11, students learn about the processes the body uses to break down proteins, carbohydrates, and lipids. Students are introduced to basal metabolism, basal metabolic rate, and a variety of factors which affect metabolism.

Metabolism takes place in all living animals. It involves a delicate balance between countless complex biological reactions.

The hearts of all mammals beat approximately the same number of times during a normal life span. A bird's heart beats very rapidly for its short life span while an elephant's heart beats much more slowly during its longer lifetime.

The metabolism of alcohol is carried out in the liver by special enzymes, which are limited in number. When an excessive quantity of alcohol enters the bloodstream, the liver is unable to metabolize it rapidly due to the limited number of enzymes available. As a result, the excess alcohol can poison the brain and cause death.

Teacher's Resource Guide
REPRODUCIBLE MATERIALS

T-13:   Factors Affecting BMR

ACTIVITIES

1. Discuss how the metabolic processes described in the chapter transform food into the energy and compounds needed by the body. Review the functions of carbohydrates, lipids, and proteins, and the information on kilocalories and weight gain and loss from Chapter 4.
2. Show the film "Diffusion and Osmosis." ENBE 1973 (14 minutes) to help students understand the concept of osmosis.
3. Have students record the foods they eat and the activities in which they participate for a specific period of time. Evaluate students' diets and activity levels by using a computer program that relates calorie intake and activity to weight gain and loss. Ask students to calculate how much more they would have to eat to gain weight at the current level of activity, how much less they would have to eat to lose weight, and how they could vary activity level to bring about these changes without a change in diet.
4. Explain what basal metabolism is and how it is measured using basal metabolic rate (BMR). Discuss the factors which can affect BMR, using **T-13: Factors Affecting BMR**. This is printed in the *Guide* and in the *Student Activity Workbook*. Ask students to compare and contrast the BMR of a young child, a teenager, a middle-aged person, and an elderly person.
5. Have students calculate their BMRs using page 97 of the *Student Activity Workbook*. The method is outlined on page 181 of *Food Science*. Ask them to calculate the number of calories used in their voluntary activities as outlined on page 183 of *Food Science*. When they add these two figures together, how does the total compare to their calorie intake as figured in Activity 3 above?
6. Show film: "Nutrition for Sports: Facts and Fallacies," HIGG, 1981 (20 minutes).
7. Have students plan menus for an athlete for the last two days before a big competition. Discuss how these menus would differ from what the athlete might eat when not training or competing.

8. Have students read and discuss the following article: Robert H. Goldsmith, "Alcohol Metabolism," *Chem Matters*, February 1985, page 8.
9. Have students use computer programs related to diet and exercise.

OVERVIEW OF EXPERIMENTS

● *Experiment 11-1*: OSMOSIS—TRAVEL THROUGH A MEMBRANE

Time Required

Day 1—10 minutes
Day 2—20 minutes
Day 3—20 minutes

Objective

Students will observe the process of osmosis by noting changes in the level of liquid surrounding raw shelled eggs and changes in the appearance of the eggs themselves.

Equipment

● 12 250-mL beakers

Supplies

● 12 small eggs
● vinegar
● corn syrup
● sodium chloride
● masking tape
● marking pen

Helpful Hints

● Demonstrate how to remove the shell from an egg after it has soaked in vinegar for three days. Hold the egg in the palm of one hand. Place it under running water and use the thumb of the other hand to gently wipe away the thin layer of shell until the membrane underneath is exposed. This must be done very carefully to avoid puncturing the membrane.

Laboratory Simplification

Perform variations 1 and 3 only.

Laboratory Enrichment

After students conduct the experiment, demonstrate that changes due to osmosis are reversible. Show students that the eggs used in the experiment can return to normal shape or can go from a shriveled to a swollen shape or the reverse.

Expected Data

Variation	Initial Liquid Height	Height/ Appearance After 30 Minutes	Height After 24 Hours	Appearance of Egg After 24 Hours	Appearance of Liquid After 24 Hours
1	5 cm	5 cm	4.5 cm	swollen	thicker, foamy
2	6 cm	6 cm	5.5 cm	swollen	thicker, foamy
3	6 cm	6 cm	6.5 cm	shriveled	runny, thin
4	6.5 cm	6.5 cm	6.5 cm	normal	clear, unchanged

● *Experiment 11-2:* KILOCALORIES IN FOOD

Time Required

45 minutes

Objective

Students will measure the amount of heat given off by a burning nut to better understand how food is converted into energy in the body.

Equipment

- 6 triple beam balances/3 electronic balances
- 12 laboratory thermometers
- 12 large corks
- 12 long needles
- 12 soup cans (used to hold water)
- 12 coffee cans or large juice cans with tops and bottoms removed. With a can opener, punch holes around the sides at one end of the cans.
- 12 stirring rods

Supplies

- box of wooden matches
- 1 package peanuts
- 1 package walnuts
- 1 package another kind of nut, if desired

Helpful Hints

- Put together a sample equipment assembly so students have a model to refer to in setting up their own equipment.
- Stress that students need to *gently* push the nut into the needle. Too much force will cause the nut to break.
- Remind students to mass the cork, needle, and nut assembly as one unit before and after burning the nut.
- Students will calculate calories per gram of nut burned from their experimental results. However, the values they will find in "calorie" charts are actually kilocalories. Therefore they will divide their experimental results by 1000 before comparing them to table values.

Laboratory Simplification

Perform the lab with one type of nut.

Laboratory Enrichment

Add the variation of a honey-roasted nut.

Expected Data

Kind of Nut	Mass			Temperature		
	Original	Final	Change	Original	Final	Change
peanut	2.2 g	1.4 g	0.8 g	27° C	44° C	17° C
walnut	2.9 g	2.3 g	0.6 g	20° C	39° C	19° C

● Experiment 11-3: DIGESTION OF STARCH

Time Required

45 minutes

Objective

Students will be able to see the effect of saliva on the digestion of starch and how digestion is affected by time and temperature.

Equipment

● 72 test tubes
● 12 water baths
● 12 thermometers

Supplies

● Tincture of iodine
● 12 g potato starch

Helpful Hints

Students may be reluctant to spit. Encourage them to make the most of the moment.

Laboratory Simplification

None.

Laboratory Enrichment

Repeat experiment using corn starch.

Expected Data

Type of Sample	Color of Sample
Original Mixture Test Tube A	creamy
Original Mixture plus iodine	blue
after 5 minutes	dark brown
after 10 minutes	yellow
after 15 minutes	yellow

ANSWER KEY

Student Text

● ANSWERS TO QUESTIONS IN TEXT:

p. 177

Carbohydrates may be broken down into glucose to be used by the body immediately, stored in the body as glycogen, or converted to fat.

p. 178

ADP uses energy provided by the breakdown of glucose to link with another phosphate group to become ATP.

p. 179

The mechanical phase of digestion takes place in the mouth.

p. 180

Being cold-blooded, a lizard would have a lower metabolic rate on a cool morning than a warm-blooded human being.

p. 183 1050 kcal.

p. 187

1. Water is the most important nutrient for athletes.
2. Carbohydrate loading may cause an abnormal heartbeat, swollen and painful muscles, and weight gain.

● CHECK YOUR FACTS

1. Glucose.
2. Anabolism and catabolism are two opposite body processes that together are metabolism.
3. Enough oxygen and water, a way to get rid of waste products, an acceptable body temperature, appropriate levels of dissolved substances in blood and cells.
4. Involves the movement of fluids across semipermeable cell membranes so the concentration of solute is the same on both sides of the membrane.
5. The amount of energy needed by the body at rest to maintain the automatic activities that support life. Basal metabolic rate measures basal metabolism as heat given off per time unit (kilocalories per hour).
6. Age, body temperature, sex, environment, body surface, and supply of nutrients.
7. Sedentary activity—80–100 kcal per hour, light activity—110–160 kcal per hour, moderate activity—170–240 kcal per hour, vigorous activity—250–350 kcal per hour, strenuous activity—over 350 kcal per hour.
8. About a day.
9. A burning sensation in the muscles or extreme muscle fatigue.
10. Their muscles burn glucose fast and efficiently, and they have a supply of the enzymes that burn fat at a fast rate.

● CRITICAL THINKING AND PROBLEM SOLVING

1. So the water can pass through the membranes to equalize the concentration of solutes.
2. Males have less body fat and more lean muscle than females. Fat tissue is less active metabolically, so females tend to have lower basal metabolism, thus a lower BMR factor.
3. No—the tall thin man will have a faster BMR because he has more body surface area.

4. It would increase—the person would have more body surface for the same amount of weight.
5. The person living in the Arctic would likely have a higher BMR to be able to maintain an acceptable body temperature in the cold environment.
6. Since running burns about 350 kcal per hour, 2450 extra kcal would be needed.
7. About 318 g (0.7 lb.) per week.

Student Activity Workbook

● H-11-1: STUDY GUIDE

1. The chemical and physical processes occurring within the living cells of the body.
2. The main component of animal and plant cells; a colloidal substance made up of protein, lipids, carbohydrates, and organic salts.
3. Anabolism and catabolism.
4. Adenosine triphosphate—ATP.
5. Bonds between the second and third phosphate groups in an ATP molecule; where the energy is carried.
6. The body temperature of warm-blooded animals is maintained at a more or less constant temperature while the body temperature of cold-blooded animals varies with the environment.
7. The metabolic rate of small animals is faster than that of large animals.
8. That varying amounts of certain substances can pass through a membrane.
9. The concentration of substances dissolved in body fluids.
10. Sodium and chloride ions.
11. Regulation of temperature, maintenance of breathing, control of the heartbeat, breaking apart molecules, and building muscle tissue.
12. By the basal metabolic rate.
13. The younger the person, the higher the BMR.
14. Basal metabolism and voluntary activities.
15. Reading, watching television or movies playing cards, typing, eating, etc.
16. Bowling, walking, golfing, gardening, scrubbing, etc.
17. Consuming nothing but fluids, usually water.
18. Ketones and ammonia.
19. From stored glycogen.
20. By eating complex carbohydrates.

H-11-2: THE METABOLISM FILE

1. anabolism
2. osmosis
3. basal metabolism
4. mammal
5. protoplasm
6. catabolism
7. fever
8. metabolism
9. voluntary
10. membrane
11. lactic acid
12. age
13. ketone
14. metabolic rate
15. adenosine triphosphate
16. complex carbohydrates
17. water
18. semipermeable
19. fasting
20. sedentary

H-11-3: CALCULATING BASAL METABOLIC RATE

Answers will vary.

H-11-4: NUTRITION AND YOU

1. Athletes require more energy than less active people because strenuous exercise requires more kilocalories than light activity.
2. Complex carbohydrates are the best source of kilocalories for athletes.
3. Glycogen is the main source of energy stored in muscles.
4. Carboloading can cause an abnormal heartbeat, swollen and painful muscles, and weight gain.
5. The most important nutrient for athletes is water.
6. Perspiration regulates body temperature.
7. Athletes do not need extra protein because it is not a good fuel for athletic activity, and there is no evidence that extra protein increases strength, endurance, or speed.
8. Eating a balanced diet with the additional carbohydrates needed for energy will ensure athletes will get an adequate supply of vitamins and minerals.
9. b
10. Answers will vary, but may include pasta, pancakes, breads and cereals.

T-13: FACTORS AFFECTING BMR

1. younger
2. male
3. large
4. cold
5. fever
6. older
7. females
8. small
9. hot
10. inadequate

Experiment 11-1: OSMOSIS—TRAVEL THROUGH A MEMBRANE

1. Answers will vary. Water goes into the egg immersed in the tap water and vinegar, while water leaves the egg in corn syrup. This is obvious from the change in the size of the egg after 24 hours. No apparent change occurs in the egg immersed in salt water.
2. They are shriveled.
3. The eggs in corn syrup lost the most water because the concentration of water was lower in the corn syrup than in the eggs. The eggs in the pure water gained the most water because the concentration of water was higher outside the eggs than inside them.

Experiment 11-2: KILOCALORIES IN FOOD

1. Answers will vary. Sample calculations for the peanut would be: 100 g $\times$ 17 $\times$ 1 calorie/degrees - gram = 1700 calories. Sample calculations for the walnut would be: 100 g $\times$ 19 $\times$ 1 calorie/degrees - gram = 1900 calories.
2. Answers will vary. Sample calculations for the peanut would be: 1700 calories/.80 g = 2125 calories = 2.1 kcal per gram. Sample calculations for the walnut would be: 1900 calories/.60 g = 3167 calories = 3.1 kcal per gram.
3. Walnut; peanut; exact quantities will vary from the values in the standard calorie tables. Results should agree with relative table value, i.e., peanuts should have a lower value than walnuts.
4. Experimental values will be less than table values because the equipment assembly was not insulated to prevent energy loss to the surroundings.

Experiment 11-3: DIGESTION OF STARCH

1. The color of the iodine is dark blue.
2. No, starch was completely gone after ten minutes.

Chapter 11: Metabolism
FACTORS AFFECTING BMR

TEXT PAGES 176–193

DIRECTIONS: Fill in the blanks below.

BMR *is higher*:

1. In _____ people.
2. For _____ .
3. For _____ people (more body surface area).
4. In a _____ environment.
5. During a _____ (increased body temperature).

BMR *is lower*:

6. In _____ people.
7. For _____ .
8. For _____ people (less body surface area).
9. In very _____ weather.
10. When _____ nutrients are consumed.

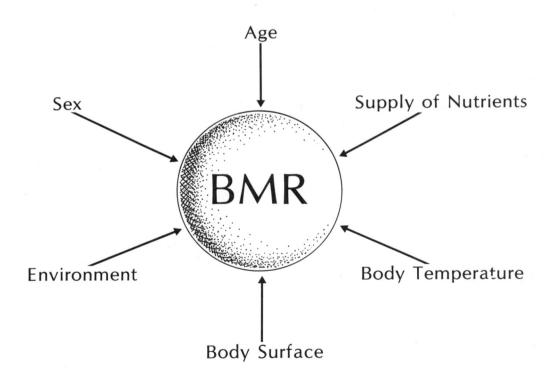

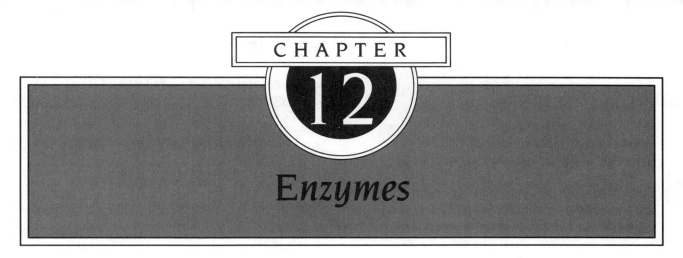

CHAPTER

12

Enzymes

TEXT PAGES 196-209

SUGGESTED TIME SCHEDULE

180-day course—9 days.
90-day course—4 days.

STUDENT OBJECTIVES

- Describe how enzymes act as catalysts in chemical reactions.
- Explain the relationship between an enzyme and a substrate.
- Compare the functions and activities of enzymes and coenzymes.
- Discuss various enzymes involved in digestion.
- Identify factors that affect enzyme activity.
- Explain how enzyme reactions are involved in food preparation.

CHAPTER SUMMARY

- Enzymes are protein catalysts that break down and put together other compounds.
- Enzymes perform specific functions on specific substrates.
- In many chemical reactions, small molecules called coenzymes are needed for an enzyme to function.
- A variety of enzymes are active during digestion to break down food so nutrients can be used by the body.
- Enzyme activity is affected by temperature, pH, and water.
- Enzymes play a desired role in baking yeast bread, tenderizing meat, and making cheese.
- Food scientists work to retard the activity of enzymes that cause enzymatic browning and food spoilage.

BACKGROUND INFORMATION

Chapter 12 focuses on enzymes—the proteins that function as catalysts in biological reactions. The chapter presents information on the nature of enzymes, how they function in the body, and why they are important to food scientists.

Enzymes are vital to living organisms. They are specific, that is, each type of enzyme serves only one purpose. In humans, enzymes control most body functions.

The chemist, H.S. Paine, invented the liquid found in chocolate candies in 1924. His discovery was based on the different solubilities of three sugars. He first placed sucrose in water to form a mixture with a paste-like consistency. He then added the enzyme invertase to the sucrose paste, placed the paste around a cherry, and coated it with chocolate. Mr. Paine maintained the chocolates at a temperature of 18°C over a period of several weeks. During this time, the invertase changed the sucrose to glucose and fructose. Since these sugars are more soluble in water than sucrose, the center of the candy became liquid. People today still enjoy the chocolate-covered cherries with the sweet liquid center that Mr. Paine invented.

Teacher's Resource Guide
REPRODUCIBLE MATERIALS

T-14:   What Is an Enzyme?

ACTIVITIES

1. Use **T-14: What Is an Enzyme?** to explain to students the characteristics and functions of enzymes. It is printed in the *Guide* and in the *Student Activity Workbook*. Point out the "lock and key" aspects of enzyme functioning.

2. Have students read and discuss: Arthur Vellin, "Enzymes," FDA *Consumer*, April 1986, page 11.

3. Have students work in pairs to create a poster that shows at least one aspect of enzyme activity. The poster should be the design for a one-page magazine advertisement to educate the public about the importance of enzymes. Possible topics include: enzymes as catalysts, enzymes and temperature, enzymes and food processing, etc.

4. Discuss with students the pros and cons of using sulfites in food preservation. As demonstrated in **Experiment 12-1: Enzymatic Browning**, sodium bisulfite is an effective means of halting enzymatic browning. However, some people are highly allergic to the compound. It is estimated that over one million people are allergic to sulfiting agents. Some of them have severe reactions which, in extreme cases, can cause death.

5. Show the film: "Nutrition: Vitamin Wise," SIMS 1982 (19 minutes).

6. Have students read and discuss one or more of the following articles:
   - Chris Lews, "Sulfite: FDA Limits Uses, Broadens Labeling," FDA *Consumer*, October 1986, page 10.
   - "Sulfites Still Here, There, and Everywhere," *Tufts University Diet and Nutrition Newsletter*, September 1986, page 1.
   - "Salads: Kept Fresh Without Sulfites," *Tufts University Diet and Nutrition Newsletter*, October 1986, page 8.

7. In preparation for **Experiment 12-1: Enzymatic Browning**, demonstrate how to prepare the fruit leather. Do not add any preservatives before pureeing the uncooked fruit. As enzymatic browning occurs, discuss its cause and prevention. When the cell walls of light colored fruits and vegetables are cut, bruised, or broken, the exposure to oxygen allows the enzymatic action that causes browning.

OVERVIEW OF EXPERIMENTS

● *Experiment* 12-1: ENZYMATIC BROWNING

Time Required

Day 1—45 minutes
Day 2—20 minutes

Objective

Students will test the effectiveness of various preservatives in preventing enzymatic browning.

Equipment

- 12 paring knives
- 12 rubber spatulas
- 12 cutting boards
- 6 medium sauce pans
- 6 blenders or food processors
- 6 triple beam balances/3 electronic balances
- 8 10-mL graduated cylinders
- food dehydrators

Supplies

- 24 apples or pears
- 1 bottle lemon juice
- 250-mg vitamin C tablets
- sodium bisulfite
- plastic wrap or dehydrator liners
- masking tape
- marking pen

Helpful Hints

- This usually is one of the students' favorite experiments. Since it is important for students to carry out the steps quickly in the proper order, it is best to demonstrate the procedures before they conduct the experiment. During the demonstration, show safe techniques for cutting and paring the fruit on a cutting board. Stress safety in using the blender or food processor.
- During your demonstration, do not use any preservatives before blending the uncooked fruit so that students can observe the enzymatic browning that occurs. Remind students that they must add the preservative assigned in their variation before they puree the fruit. Otherwise it will be too late to prevent browning.

- Sodium bisulfite can usually be purchased at a fermenting store or at some pharmacies. Be sure to stress that sodium bisulfite causes an allergic reaction in some people. Therefore, students will not taste the samples treated with sodium bisulfite.
- Do not use Golden Delicious apples for this experiment—they tend not to brown as much as other varieties. Have fruit at room temperature at the beginning of the experiment, since the enzymes work more slowly if the fruit is cold.
- Many apples are "sealed" during processing to keep them from drying out. Because of the presence of this sealant, apples should always be washed before eating.
- Depending on the number and type of food dehydrators available for use, you may have to return to school in the evening to check on the progress of the fruit leathers.

Laboratory Simplification

Do fewer variations.

Laboratory Enrichment

Repeat with a second type of fruit.

Expected Data

Variation	Color	Texture	Flavor
1	golden	smooth	good, tangy
2	dark gold to rust	chunky	slightly bitter
3	bright yellow	smooth	—
4	bright yellow	chunky	—
5	golden to rust	smooth	good
6	mustard to rust	chunky	acidic flavor
Puree from Tchr. Demo.	brown	chunky	apple

Results will vary depending on the temperature of the fruit, the variety of apples used, and student handling of the fruit.

● *Experiment* 12-2: EFFECT OF BLANCHING ON ENZYMES

Time Required

Day 1—30 minutes
Day 2—25 minutes (five weeks later)

Objective

Students will observe the effects of blanching on the quality of frozen food.

Equipment

- 12 large sauce pans
- 12 knives
- peelers—optional

Supplies

- fruits and vegetables of choice
- 24 freezer bags
- masking tape
- marking pen

Helpful Hints

- Produce recommended for this experiment includes asparagus (which has the most noticeable change), broccoli, cauliflower, potatoes, or carrots.
- This experiment needs to be conducted at least five weeks before the end of the term so that noticeable enzyme activity can take place.
- Be certain students accurately label their samples.
- After the food has been removed from the freezer, thawed, and cooked, students should carry out a sensory evaluation. Bite-sized pieces of each sample should be evaluated with the results recorded in the students' data tables.

Laboratory Simplification

Use three different types of vegetables only.

Laboratory Enrichment

Add two variations in step 4: boil for one minute only and boil for five minutes.

Expected Data

In general, samples of blanched vegetables will have a better flavor, more pleasant aroma, brighter color, and firmer texture than unblanched samples of the same vegetable.

ANSWER KEY
Student Text

• ANSWERS TO QUESTIONS IN TEXT:

p. 198
A catalyst lowers the amount of the activation energy required for a reaction.

p. 201
Amylase is the enzyme that converts amylose to the sugar maltose. Two enzymes found in the stomach are rennin and pepsin. Rennin curdles milk protein and prepares it for pepsin which denatures protein by attacking the peptide bonds.

p. 202
Amylase makes rice less sticky.

p. 203
Factors that affect the rate of enzyme action are temperature, pH, and the amount of an enzyme.

• CHECK YOUR FACTS

1. Enzymes.
2. They are used to break food into compounds the body can use for nourishment.
3. They are made of protein and serve the function of any catalyst—they help chemical reactions occur without being used up by the reaction.
4. They help the reaction occur but are not used up so are able to take part in another reaction.
5. A substance on which an enzyme reacts.
6. For the substrates on which they react. The suffix "ase" is added to the substrate name to show the substance is an enzyme.
7. The enzymes often couldn't react if the coenzyme weren't there.
8. Digest food by breaking it down; build new molecules from the products of digestion.
9. Temperature, pH, water.
10. 8.5

11. In baking bread, tenderizing meat, cheese making, and controlling rates of reaction.
12. Heating, lowering the pH, lowering the temperature, using sulfur dioxide.

• CRITICAL THINKING AND PROBLEM SOLVING

1. Disaccharides, galactose, and peptides.
2. They lower activation energy so the reaction can occur at a lower temperature.
3. Both act to digest protein. However, those in the stomach work in a strongly acid environment while those in the small intestine function in a neutral environment.
4. Blanching food denatures the enzymes that would cause the food to turn brown or become bitter.
5. No—the acid used to pickle the cucumbers would denature the enzymes.
6. Sucrase from the yeast breaks down the sucrose in the bread to form carbon dioxide, which causes the bread to rise.
7. It attacks the connective tissue in muscle fiber, breaking it down and making it easier to eat.
8. Fresh pineapple contains an enzyme that digests the protein gelatin so it will not set. The heat used in canning pineapple denatures the enzyme so it does not act on the gelatin. The gelatin can then set normally.
9. The banana slices could be dipped in lemon juice or ascorbic acid solution before being pureed.

Student Activity Workbook

• H-12-1: STUDY GUIDE

1.	enzymes	14.	temperature
2.	catalyst	15.	denatured
3.	active site	16.	bitter
4.	activation energy	17.	8.5
5.	lower	18.	sucrase
6.	coenzymes	19.	sucrose
7.	thiamin	20.	sucrase
8.	mouth	21.	papain
9.	amylase	22.	tender
10.	rennin	23.	enzymatic browning
11.	pancreatic juice	24.	lowering
12.	proteins	25.	salt
13.	coagulating		

• H-12-2: MAGIC SQUARE

A.	8	**D.**	1	**G.**	6
B.	3	**E.**	5	**H.**	7
C.	4	**F.**	9	**I.**	2

The magic number is 15.

• H-12-3: ANALOGIES

1. a
2. c
3. a
4. d
5. b
6. a
7. b
8. a
9. c
10. d

• H-12-4: CROSSWORD PUZZLE

Across
2. substrate
4. activation energy
6. catalyst
12. enzymatic browning
14. amylase
15. sucrase
16. lactase

Down
1. enzymes
3. blanched
5. curd
7. active site
8. pepain
9. rennin/pepsin
10. coenzymes
11. glucose
13. glycine

• H-12-5: NUTRITION AND YOU

1. mouth
2. acidic
3. amylose, maltose
4. sodium bicarbonate
5. sweet
6. stomach
7. pepsin
8. rennin, pepsin
9. proteases, lipases, carbohydrates
10. lipase enzyme

• T-14: WHAT IS AN ENZYME?

1. protein
2. chemical
3. catalyst
4. substrates
5. active
6. substrate
7. reduce
8. coenzyme
9. deactivated

• Experiment 12-1: ENZYMATIC BROWNING

1. In the uncooked, untreated fruit leather prepared during the teacher's demonstration. In the experiment, in the uncooked fruit leather treated with ascorbic acid. The cooked fruit leather treated with sodium bisulfite. By the color of the final product—a darker color shows more enzyme activity.
2. The color was preserved best by the cooked method. Heat decreased the enzyme activity.
3. Sodium bisulfite.
4. The fruit leather treated with lemon juice.
5. Yes—the fruit leather prepared from the cooked fruit was smoother.
6. The cooked method using the sodium bisulfite produced the best fruit leather.

• Experiment 12-2: EFFECT OF BLANCHING ON ENZYMES

1. It denatures the enzymes that would cause the vegetables to turn brown and spoil while frozen.
2. To keep them from being cooked by the blanching process.
3. The blanched method produced vegetables with the better color, aroma, texture, and taste.
4. Enzyme activity in the unblanched sample created undesirable changes.

Chapter 12: Enzymes

WHAT IS AN ENZYME?

TEXT PAGES 196~209

DIRECTIONS: Fill in the blanks below.

An enzyme:

1. Is a _____ molecule.

2. Controls specific _____ activity in living organisms.

3. Acts as a _____ in reactions.

4. Reacts with substances called _____.

5. Attaches to the substrate at the enzyme's _____ site.

6. Is named for the particular _____ on which it acts.

7. _____ the activation energy needed to start a reaction.

8. May need a _____ to function.

9. Is _____ by heat or low or high pH.

CHAPTER
13

Solutions, Colloidal Dispersions, and Emulsions

TEXT PAGES 210-233

SUGGESTED TIME SCHEDULE

180-day course—8 days.
90-day course—4 days.

STUDENT OBJECTIVES

- Identify the solvent and solute in a given solution.
- Discuss the effect of a solute and its concentration on the boiling and freezing points of a solution.
- Calculate the concentration of a solution using mass percent.
- Compare and contrast unsaturated, saturated, and supersaturated solutions.
- Describe the properties of colloidal dispersions.
- Explain the three parts of an emulsion and their relationship to each other.
- Identify various food emulsions and tell the type of emulsion each is.

CHAPTER SUMMARY

- Solutions are homogeneous mixtures in which a solute is dissolved in a solvent.
- The concentration of a solute affects the solution's boiling and freezing points.
- The concentration of a solution can be measured by calculating mass percent.
- Gas-in-liquid solutions become less soluble when heated, while solid-in-liquid solutions become more soluble when heated.
- The particles in a colloidal dispersion are larger than those in a solution and will scatter light in the Tyndall effect.

- An emulsion consists of a dispersed phase mixed in a continuous phase, with an emulsifier to hold the two phases in the mixture.
- Oil-in-water emulsions include salad dressings and mayonnaise, air-in-liquid emulsions include egg foams and whipped cream, while butter and margarine are water-in-oil emulsions.

BACKGROUND INFORMATION

Chapter 13 provides more information about water, solutions, colloidal dispersions, and emulsions. Students will learn the characteristics of the three types of mixtures and the role each plays in food preparation.

The formula weight of an ionic substance in grams, known as a mole, will change the freezing point or boiling point of a solution at least twice as much as a mole of a molecular substance. This is because a change in boiling or freezing point depends on the number of particles in solution. Each mole of an ionic substance breaks up into at least one mole of positive ions and one mole of negative ions. A mole of molecular substance simply yields one mole of molecules in solution.

Protein molecules never form true solutions because they are too large to do so. It is impossible for enough of them to disperse in 1 mL water to produce colligative properties, such as the boiling point elevation and freezing point depression characteristic of true solutions.

Lecithin, found in egg yolk, is an excellent emulsifier. It is a bipolar phospholipid molecule with one end that is polar, and therefore attracted to water

109

molecules, and one end that is nonpolar, so it is attracted to other nonpolar molecules such as oil.

In an oil-and-water emulsion, what is referred to as the water phase can be vinegar, lemon juice, fruit juice, or milk—any liquid that is mostly water.

Teacher's Resource Guide
REPRODUCIBLE MATERIALS

T-15:   Do You Know the Difference?
E-13-A: Salt and Homemade Ice Cream

ACTIVITIES

1. Show film: "Chemistry: Solutions," CORO, 1983 (23 minutes) to introduce students to the properties of solutions. Use **T-15: Do You Know the Difference?** to clarify the differences among solutions, colloidal dispersions, and emulsions. It is printed in the *Guide* and in the *Student Activity Workbook*.

2. Review with students the differences between homogeneous and heterogeneous mixtures and between ionic and molecular solids. Discuss the properties of solutions and the behavior of ionic and molecular solids when they dissolve in water.

3. Explain to students the concept of mass percent as a means of calculating the concentration of solutions. Demonstrate how to perform mass percent problems.

4. Discuss the properties of colloidal dispersions and demonstrate the Tyndall effect. In a darkened room, shine the beam from a strong flashlight (or the light in a projector) through gelatin that is in a clear glass container. The beam shows up best if the gelatin is red.

5. Discuss the properties of emulsions with students. Demonstrate the behavior of two miscible liquids, such as apple juice and water, and two immiscible liquids, such as oil and water. Explain the role of an emulsifier in an emulsion.

6. In preparation for **Experiment 13-1: Boiling Points of Sugar and Salt Solutions**, heat some of the sugar solution to demonstrate that the mixture will turn brown (caramelize) at about 160°C.

7. In preparation for **Experiment 13-2: Making an Emulsion**, demonstrate the techniques for making the mayonnaise, especially the correct procedure for adding the oil.

EXTENSION ACTIVITIES

1. Have students perform **Experiment 13-A: Salt and Homemade Ice Cream**.

2. While students are performing **Experiment 13-A: Salt and Homemade Ice Cream**, place a sample of the cream mixture in the freezer and allow it to freeze. Compare the quality of the frozen product with the stirred mixtures the students prepare.

3. Have students repeat **Experiment 13-A: Salt and Homemade Ice Cream** mixing other substances with the ice instead of sodium chloride. Possible substitutes could include calcium chloride, calcium carbonate, methyl alcohol, or mineral oil. Determine which substance(s) will cool the mixture sufficiently to produce ice cream.

OVERVIEW OF EXPERIMENTS

● *Experiment* 13-1: BOILING POINTS OF SUGAR AND SALT SOLUTIONS

Time Required

35 minutes

Objective

Students will observe that water solutions do not boil at the same temperature as pure water and that boiling point varies with the solution's concentration.

Equipment

- 12 250-mL beakers
- 12 candy thermometers
- clock or watch with a second hand

Supplies

- 2000 mL sodium chloride solution (see below)
- 2000 mL sucrose solution (see below)

Helpful Hints

- To make the sodium chloride solution, dissolve 725 g sodium chloride in 2000 mL water or 36.25 g per 100 mL water.

- To make the sucrose solution, dissolve 4220 grams sucrose in 2000 mL water or 211 g per 100 mL water.
- Prepare the solutions in advance and have them at room temperature at the beginning of the experiment. Label the solutions using triple-digit numbers so students will not know which solution they are using. For example, the salt solution can be #417 and the sucrose solution #853.
- Candy thermometers with both Fahrenheit and Celsius degrees are needed for this experiment.
- The sugar solution will turn brown at about 160°C, while the salt solution will display crystal formation around the sides of the beaker as the water boils away.
- Students will need to use plenty of warm soapy water to clean up the equipment after this experiment.
- Have graph paper available so students can begin drawing their graphs as soon as they have finished cleaning up their work areas and equipment.

Laboratory Simplification

In step 3, take readings every 60 seconds.

Laboratory Enrichment

None.

Expected Data

The salt solution boils at approximately 115°C throughout the experiment. The concentration remains nearly the same because the extra salt crystallizes out as the water evaporates.

The sucrose solution displays an ever-increasing boiling point throughout the experiment since the solubility of sucrose increases as the temperature increases, so the mixture becomes more concentrated as the water evaporates.

● *Experiment* 13-2: MAKING AN EMULSION

Time Required

45 minutes

Objective

Students will compare the properties of emulsions prepared using a variety of methods of adding the oil to the other ingredients.

Equipment

- 12 small containers for egg whites
- 12 small containers for egg yolks
- 12 small bowls
- 12 electric mixers (or blenders or food processors)
- 12 100-mL graduated cylinders
- 12 250-mL beakers
- 6 triple beam balances/3 electronic balances

Supplies

- 24 eggs
- sodium chloride
- dry mustard
- 3 L salad oil
- 600 mL vinegar

Helpful Hints

- As you demonstrate the techniques needed to conduct this experiment, encourage students to notice the color change that occurs when the vinegar is added. Discuss the proper use of the equipment used to prepare the emulsion—electric mixers, blenders, or food processors.
- Have all groups use the same-sized equipment.
- Have all ingredients at room temperature at the beginning of the experiment.
- Use large egg yolks.

Laboratory Simplification

Do variations 1 and 4 only.

Laboratory Enrichment

1. Repeat experiment with temperature as the variable. The ingredients could be cold, at room temperature, and heated. Use the procedure in variation 1, and keep the quantities the same.
2. Repeat experiment while varying the amount of oil added. Use the procedure in variation 1.
3. Repeat experiment with half of the class using only one egg yolk while the other half of the class uses two egg yolks. Use the procedure in variation 1.

Expected Data

Variation	Color	Appearance	Flavor	Texture
1	creamy white	smooth	tangy	smooth
2	creamy yellow	some separation	tangy	lumpy
3	creamy yellow	separated a bit	oily tangy	slightly runny
4	yellowish	liquid	oily	runny

● Experiment 13-A: SALT AND HOMEMADE ICE CREAM

Note: The procedure for this experiment is printed only in the *Teacher's Resource Guide*.

Time Required

45 minutes

Objective

Students will discover the role of salt in the preparation of homemade ice cream.

Equipment

- plastic container for preparing mixture
- 12 thermometers
- 24 stirring rods

Supplies

- 1 bag crushed ice
- 1000 mL cold 18 percent cream
- 250 mL sugar
- 4 mL vanilla
- 720 mL salt
- 12 75 mL/or 3 oz wax-coated paper cups
- 12 300- to 350-mL styrofoam cups

Helpful Hints

- Prepare the cream mixture before class by mixing the cream, sugar, and vanilla together in a plastic container.
- Have half the class add salt to the ice and half the class use ice alone.

Expected Data

The ice will remain at 0°C if salt is not added. The cream mixture will not freeze.

If salt is added, the ice/salt mixture will cool to approximately -15°C and the ice cream will form.

ANSWER KEY

Student Text

● ANSWERS TO QUESTIONS IN TEXT:

p. 212

The greater the surface area and the longer the cooking time, the greater the loss of vitamins and minerals.

p. 212

1. In addition to preventing tooth decay, fluoride appears to slow the loss of bone in osteoporosis.
2. Answers will vary.

p. 219

Both egg foam and whipped cream are gas-in-liquid colloidal dispersions.

p. 220

Egg yolk is the emulsifier in mayonnaise.

● CHECK YOUR FACTS

1. 40 g/90 g × 100 = 44 percent.
2. It contains 10 g orange juice for every 90 g water.
3. Hot tea—the heat increases the amount of sugar that dissolves before the solution becomes saturated.
4. Add more water or heat the solution.

5. In the size of their particles—the other differing properties such as effect on boiling or freezing points or the Tyndall effect result from particle size.

6. It holds two immiscible liquids together. It can do this either by adsorbing to the surface of the dispersed phase, lowering its surface tension so that the droplets cannot stick together, or by having one end of its molecule dissolve in the water phase and one end in the oil phase.

7. To break up the oil phase and to disperse it in the water phase. Then the emulsifier can be added to prevent the oil from separating out again.

8. By adding more water.

9. One end of a soap molecule dissolves in fats and oils and the other end dissolves in water. This draws the fats and oils off dishes and into the dishwater.

● CRITICAL THINKING AND PROBLEM SOLVING

1. Water is the solvent and sugar is the solute.

2. The freezing point of a water solution is below the freezing point of pure water; the boiling point of such a solution is higher than the boiling point of pure water.

3. Mass percent.

4. At a given temperature, an unsaturated solution does not contain all the solute it could contain, a saturated solution contains all the solute it can contain, and a supersaturated solution contains more solute than it normally would.

5. It decreases; it increases.

6. A beam of light that can be seen as it passes through a colloidal dispersion.

7. No—salt water is a solution in which the particles are too small to scatter light.

8. No—they can mix with each other.

9. An emulsion—it contains two immiscible liquids.

10. Water (vinegar).

11. Starch.

Student Activity Workbook

● H-13-1: STUDY GUIDE

1. homogeneous
2. the same
3. formula
4. two
5. gases
6. rises (increases)
7. cooking times
8. dividing
9. unsaturated
10. saturated
11. temperature
12. supersaturated
13. enamel
14. distributed or dispersed
15. size
16. aggregate
17. scatter or deflect
18. colloidal dispersion
19. almost no
20. immiscible
21. colloidal dispersion
22. surface tension
23. water
24. emulsifier
25. dispersed phase
26. continuous phase
27. gas-in-liquid
28. Homogenization
29. Butter
30. 80

● H-13-2: CROSSWORD PUZZLE

Across
1. homogeneous
4. colloidal
7. dispersed
8. immiscible
10. solvent
13. supersaturated
16. solubility
17. floats
18. yolk
19. starch

Down
2. solute
3. emulsifier
4. continuous
5. liquid
6. Tyndall
9. saturated
11. foam
12. lecithin
14. tension
15. butter

● H-13-3: NUTRITION AND YOU

1. Fluorine is found in the body as fluoride ions.

2. When fluoride is present in water in concentrations greater than one part per million, there is a noticeable decline in the rate of tooth decay among those who drink the water.

3. Fluoride helps make the enamel, the outer layer of a tooth, more resistant to decay.

4. Fluoride also may slow the loss of bone in osteoporosis.

5. Some people fear that consuming too much fluoride could be harmful. Others believe it is unnatural to add fluoride ions to water.

6a. If fluoride is present in excess of 2.5 parts per million, it can cause mottled, or discolored enamel on teeth.

6b. This is not a health problem, since the mottled teeth are very resistant to decay.

7. To protect your teeth from decay if you live in area that does not have fluoride in its water supply, you can use a fluoride toothpaste, take fluoride

tablets, or have your dentist treat your teeth with a fluoridated substance.

8. Dental fluoride treatments are generally only carried out on people who are between 3 and 16 years of age.
9. Answers will vary.

● T-15: DO YOU KNOW THE DIFFERENCE?

1. homogeneous
2. solvent
3. higher, lower
4. saturated
5. coffee, tea, carbonated beverage
6. solute particles
7. larger
8. Tyndall effect
9. no
10. gelatin, milk, jelly
11. liquid-in-liquid
12. emulsifier
13. deflect
14. mayonnaise, butter, margarine, homogenized milk

● Experiment 13-1: BOILING POINTS OF SUGAR AND SALT SOLUTIONS

1. No—higher.
2. Answers will vary. Those students who had the salt solution will report a constant temperature while those who had the sugar will report that the temperature continued to rise because the solution became more concentrated as time passed.
3. Salt was crystallizing out, causing the concentration of the solution to remain the same.

4. The lines on the graphs of the sugar solutions gradually rose while the lines on the graphs of the salt solutions stayed level. The boiling point of the sugar solutions continued to rise because of the increase in concentration while the boiling point of the salt solutions stayed the same.
5. Solutions have a higher boiling point than pure water.
6. The higher the concentration, the higher the boiling point.

● Experiment 13-2: MAKING AN EMULSION

1. Information in data table.
2. The more slowly the oil was added, the better the mayonnaise.
3. Variation 1.
4. By surrounding the droplets of oil and lowering their surface tension so that they cannot join together and separate from the vinegar.

Teacher's Resource Guide

● Experiment 13-A: SALT AND HOMEMADE ICE CREAM

1. Yes—it is necessary to add the salt to form a solution whose freezing point is below 0°C, otherwise the cream mixture won't freeze.
2. Yes—anything that will dissolve in water and lower its freezing point could be used.

Chapter 13: Solutions, Colloidal Dispersions, and Emulsions
DO YOU KNOW THE DIFFERENCE?

TEXT PAGES 210-223

DIRECTIONS: Fill in the blanks below.

A *solution*...

1. Is a _____ mixture.

2. Is a solute dissolved in a _____.

3. Has a _____ boiling point and a _____ freezing point than a pure solvent.

4. Can be unsaturated, _____, or supersaturated.

5. Can be _____, _____, or a _____ _____.

A *colloidal dispersion*...

6. Is a mixture in which the _____ _____ are dispersed (not dissolved) in the solvent.

7. Contains _____ particles than a solution.

8. Can scatter light in the _____ _____.

9. Has _____ effect on boiling or freezing points.

10. Can be _____, _____, or _____.

An *emulsion*...

11. Is a _____ dispersion.

12. Is made from two immiscible liquids and an _____.

13. Can _____ light, creating an opaque milky appearance.

14. Can be _____, _____, _____, or _____.

EXPERIMENT 13-A
Salt and Homemade Ice Cream

To prepare homemade ice cream, a mixture of cream and other ingredients is cooled to a point where the water in the cream freezes. Stirring the cream mixture is important because stirring keeps the ingredients evenly distributed as air is introduced into the mixture. The air makes the final product softer and more pleasant to eat. In this experiment, you will observe the function of salt in preparing homemade ice cream.

PROCEDURE

1. Fill a wax–coated paper cup two–thirds full of the cream mixture provided by your teacher.
2. Fill a styrofoam cup one–third full of crushed ice. Take the temperature of the ice, and record it in your data table.
3. Follow the variation assigned by your teacher.

   a. **Variation 1.** Go to step 4.
   b. **Variation 2.** Add 60 mL salt to the ice and stir with a stirring rod. Take the temperature of the ice, and record in your data table.

4. Set the wax–coated cup down into the icy slush in the styrofoam cup. Be sure the ice comes up around the sides of the smaller cup but does not get into the cream mixture.
5. Using a second stirring rod, stir the cream mixture slowly, scraping the newly formed crystals from the bottom and sides of the cup. Stop from time to time to let the ice cream solidify. Stir the mixture for 25 minutes. Describe the final product in your data table.
6. The groups that used salt should compare their final products with the final products of the groups that did not.

QUESTIONS

1. Is it necessary to add salt to the ice? Why?
2. Could anything other than salt (sodium chloride) be used for the same purpose as the salt?

SAMPLE DATA TABLE

Variation	Initial Temperature of Ice	Temperature of Ice and Salt	Consistency of Final Product
1		—	
2			

Leavening Agents and Baked Goods

TEXT PAGES 224–237

SUGGESTED TIME SCHEDULE

180-day course—8 days.
90-day course—4 days.

STUDENT OBJECTIVES

- Describe the purpose of leavening agents in baked goods.
- List the four major leavening agents.
- Explain why baking soda is used with an acid in baked goods.
- Identify the types of doughs and batters used in making quick breads.
- List the ingredients in baking powder.
- Discuss how air and steam act as leavening agents.
- Describe the properties of yeast as a leavening agent.
- Name three types of wheat and a product made from each.

CHAPTER SUMMARY

- Leavening involves the production of gas to cause baked goods to rise and become light and porous.
- The most common leavening agents are chemical agents, air, steam, and yeast.
- Baking soda is combined with acid to produce carbon dioxide in a two–step process.
- Baking powder is made from baking soda, dry acid, and a filler, usually cornstarch or calcium carbonate.
- Quick breads are classified as pour batters, drop batters, soft doughs, and stiff doughs depending on the ratio of liquid to flour.
- Double–acting baking powders react first with cold liquid and then with heat.

- Most products leavened primarily with air are made with egg foams.
- Yeast ferments sugar to produce the carbon dioxide used in leavening.

BACKGROUND INFORMATION

Chapter 14 introduces students to common leavening agents and their function in making baked goods lighter. Chemical leavening agents (baking soda and baking powder) and natural leavening agents (steam, air, and yeast) are discussed.

Leavening agents get their name from the verb "leaven" which means to make light and porous. Without leavening agents, baked goods would often be hard and heavy instead of light and airy. Both chemical and natural leavening agents release carbon dioxide which provides the leavening effect.

Generally speaking, any recipe that calls for baking soda also requires an acid. This acid can be citrus juice, brown sugar, molasses, honey, buttermilk, or vinegar. Baking soda and an acid can be substituted for baking powder in any recipe that calls for double-acting baking powder.

Teacher's Resource Guide
REPRODUCIBLE MATERIALS

T-16:   Leavening Agents

ACTIVITIES

1. Provide students with recipes for popovers, muffins, coffee cake, angel food cake, and yeast bread. Have students identify the type of leavening agent found in each recipe. Use **T-16: Leavening Agents** to reinforce the variety of leavening agents that can be used in baked goods. This is printed in the *Guide* and in the *Student Activity Workbook*.

2. Discuss how chemical leavening agents work. Use the chemical formulas and equations to help students understand how the production of carbon dioxide differs in different leavening agents.

3. Discuss yeast and other natural leavening agents. Show both dry and compressed yeast and demonstrate how they are handled before being added to a recipe.

4. Show the film: "Earth Bread: A Natural Food," BUFI, 1973 (20 minutes).

5. Have students experiment with freezing yeast dough at various points in the process of making the dough. Compare and evaluate the final products.

6. Organize a field trip to a commercial bakery. Have students be alert to how ingredients are measured in a commercial operation. If possible, ask a food scientist on the bakery staff to discuss the controls necessary to insure the proper growth of yeast used in making yeast bread products.

7. Have students prepare a favorite recipe for a baked product, using a leavening agent not specified in the recipe. How does the final experimental product compare in lightness and taste to the customary product? If the substitute leavening agent did not produce a satisfactory product, why not?

8. In preparation for **Experiment 14-2: Production of Carbon Dioxide Using Baking Powders**, demonstrate the procedures students will use in conducting the experiment. This will help students see how much foam is produced and help them know how to make their height measurements.

OVERVIEW OF EXPERIMENTS

● **Experiment 14-1: COMPARISON OF LEAVENING AGENTS**

Time Required

Day 1—45 minutes
Day 2—20 minutes

Objective

Students will evaluate the effect of various leavening agents in a baked product.

Equipment

● 6 triple beam balances/3 electronic balances
● 12 sifters
● 12 mixing bowls
● 12 electric mixers
● 12 23-cm (9-in.) round cake pans
● 12 knives

Supplies

● 1800 g sugar
● 1300 g cake flour
● sodium chloride
● 570 g hydrogenated shortening
● 1440 mL milk
● vanilla
● 12 eggs
● double-acting baking powder
● baking soda
● cream of tartar
● vinegar
● 240 mL buttermilk
● pH indicator paper with 1–11 range
● waxed paper
● paper towels
● plastic wrap
● marking pen

Helpful Hints

● Assign one of the variations to each laboratory group. Stress that this is a long experiment and that students will be pressed for time to complete the first part of it in one class period. Students will need to mass ingredients as quickly as possible.

● It may be necessary for you to remove the cakes from the ovens after the end of the period. Cakes should be covered overnight to keep them from drying out before students have a chance to evaluate them.

● When discussing the results of this experiment, it is important to emphasize that there are many more variables in this experiment than the specific one tested (i.e., the leavening agent). For example, how long experimenters beat the batter, how hard the batter was beaten if done by hand, the freshness of the ingredients, and the accuracy of the oven temperature could all affect the quality of the baked product. Therefore, it is very difficult to be certain that the leavening agent used caused all the differences among the samples. Students should realize that results may be inconclusive when many variables are present.

Laboratory Simplification

Do variations 1, 2, and 3 only.

Laboratory Enrichment

Use similar variations using a different cake recipe.

Expected Data

Variation	Height	Texture	Tenderness	Flavor	Moistness	pH
1	2.0 cm	heavy, sticky	tough	very sweet	very dry	4.5
2	3.6 cm	light, very fluffy	tender	good	moist	5.0
3	3.0 cm	light, fluffy	slightly tough	bland	slightly dry	5.0
4	3.0 cm	light, fluffy	tender	good	moist	5.0
5	2.7 cm	light, very fluffy	tender	slightly acid	moist	5.0
6	2.3 cm	heavy	tough	flat	very dry	5.5

● *Experiment* 14-2: PRODUCTION OF CARBON DIOXIDE USING BAKING POWDERS

Time Required

45 minutes

Objective

Students will compare the approximate amounts of carbon dioxide released from three leavening agents.

Equipment

- 24 50-mL or 100-mL graduated cylinders
- 36 250-mL beakers
- 6 triple beam balances/3 electronic balances
- 12 saucepans
- 12 plastic metric rulers

Supplies

- 2 different brands baking powder
- baking soda
- cream of tartar
- pH indicator paper with 1–11 range
- albumin solution (see below)

Helpful Hints

- Review the procedure for massing solids on paper. Remind students that the leavening agents should not be massed directly on the balance pan.
- The albumin solution can be made by separating egg whites and straining them through cheese cloth. Reconstituted dried egg whites can also be used. One source of dried egg whites is the packet in an angel food cake mix. Add 1600 mL water to the egg whites in one packet, and mix on the lowest speed of the blender. This will provide enough albumin solution for 24 laboratory groups (two classes).

- Prepare the albumin solution before class begins because students will need the full class period to complete the experiment.
- While it might seem logical that the carbon dioxide released in this experiment would cause the solution to become more acid, in general, the pH of the solution stays about the same over the course of the experiment.

Laboratory Simplification

Eliminate homemade version of baking powder.

Laboratory Enrichment

Repeat experiment with temperature as the variable. Use one baking powder and compare gas production at 10°C, 40°C, and 60°C. The results will vary depending on the exact temperatures used.

Expected Data

Note: #1 = Clabber Girl; #2 = Calumet; #3 = homemade baking powder.

Time	Height at Room Temperature			pH at Room Temperature			Height in Warm Water			pH in Warm Water		
	#1	#2	#3	#1	#2	#3	#1	#2	#3	#1	#2	#3
1 minute	2.1 cm	1.0 cm	3.5 cm	8	8.5	8	2.8 cm	1.3 cm	5.8 cm	8	8.5	8
2 minutes	2.6 cm	1.1 cm	4.4 cm	8	8.5	8	4.3 cm	2.4 cm	6.7 cm	8	8.5	8
3 minutes	2.6 cm	1.1 cm	5.0 cm	8	8.5	8	4.9 cm	2.8 cm	7.2 cm	8	8.5	8
4 minutes	2.6 cm	1.1 cm	5.0 cm	8	8.5	8	5.8 cm	3.5 cm	8.1 cm	8	8.5	8
5 minutes	2.8 cm	1.1 cm	5.0 cm	8	8.5	8	6.3 cm	4.3 cm	8.5 cm	8	8.5	8

ANSWER KEY

Student Text

● ANSWERS TO QUESTIONS IN TEXT:

p. 225
Unless ammonium bicarbonate can escape, the final product will have an unpleasant taste. That's why it's used in thin products with a large surface area, like crackers.

p. 227 Answers will vary.

p. 229 Answers will vary.

p. 231
Beer froth was used by the English in the 1700s as a leavening agent.

p. 233
Common wheat is best for making bread. Bread is considered a nutrient dense food because it provides a relatively high quantity of one or more nutrients with a relatively low number of kilocalories.

● CHECK YOUR FACTS

1. To lighten or aerate them.
2. Baking powder and baking soda.
3. Sodium carbonate is one of the products of the breakdown of $NaHCO_3$. It has an unpleasant flavor to be avoided.
4. Pour batters, drop batters, soft doughs, and stiff doughs.
5. From baking soda and cream of tartar.
6. Single-acting baking powder releases carbon dioxide as soon as a liquid is added to it. Double-acting baking powder contains two acids, one that releases carbon dioxide when a cold liquid is added to it and another that does not react until it is heated.
7. Air—angel food or sponge; steam and air—pound; chemical agents—shortened.

8. From the vaporization of liquid in the baked product.

9. The organisms other than yeast that are present in the starter (or dough).

10. It evaporates during baking.

11. By adding more yeast or more sugar.

12. It contains more moisture than the dry form and is not as stable over time.

● CRITICAL THINKING AND PROBLEM SOLVING

1. To change the chemical reaction so that sodium carbonate is not formed.

2. Lemon juice, buttermilk, or another acidic liquid.

3. It is a salt that remains in the product but does not affect flavor or cause other undesirable side effects.

4. A double-acting baking powder—at least part of it would not react until actually heated during baking. A single-acting baking powder could release all its carbon dioxide as it absorbed moisture while sitting in the cupboard.

5. To meet the legal standard of producing 12 g carbon dioxide from 100 g baking powder.

6. There needs to be enough water in the batter to provide steam to properly leaven the final product.

7. Denatured protein in the beaten egg whites.

8. The yeast are killed by the high temperature.

9. Use more yeast, more sugar, or less salt. Allow the bread to rise at a warmer temperature than had previously been used.

Student Activity Workbook

● H-14-1: STUDY GUIDE

1. gas
2. carbon dioxide gas
3. yeast
4. sodium bicarbonate
5. ammonia
6. NaHCO₃
7. when mixed with a liquid acid
8. yellowish
9. acid
10. potassium bitartrate
11. KHC₄H₄O₆
12. quick
13. pour
14. two
15. tunnels
16. pie crust or pasta
17. filler (starch)
18. Single-acting
19. double-acting
20. double-acting
21. 12
22. air and steam
23. yeast
24. Pour
25. hot

26. gluten
27. fermentation
28. sugar
29. 27
30. *Saccharomyces cerevisiae*
31. 9
32. legume or seed product
33. nutrient dense

● H-14-2: HIDDEN WORD PUZZLE

1. double-acting
2. fermentation
3. carbon dioxide
4. air
5. pour
6. soft
7. common
8. nutrient dense
9. sodium bicarbonate
10. knead
11. durum
12. baking soda
13. acid
14. single-acting
15. leavening
16. drop
17. gluten
18. yeast
19. steam
20. stiff
21. shortened
22. club
23. quick
24. baking powder
25. pound

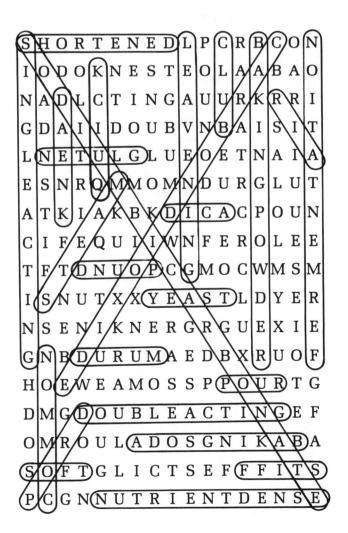

H-14-3: ANALOGIES

1. c
2. b
3. d
4. b
5. c
6. b
7. b
8. c
9. b
10. b

H-14-4: NUTRITION AND YOU

1. 10,000 years ago
2. nutritive
3. Herodotus
4. two-thirds
5. common, club, durum
6. common
7. cake
8. nutrient dense
9. protein
10. more, fiber

T-16: LEAVENING AGENTS

1. yeast
2. egg protein and hot air
3. baking powder
4. egg protein and hot air
5. baking soda and liquid acid
6. baking powder
7. egg protein and hot air
8. ammonium bicarbonate
9. baking powder

Experiment 14-1: COMPARISON OF LEAVENING AGENTS

1. Information in data table.
2. Information in data table.
3. Answers will vary. No generalizations can be made due to the large number of variables present.
4. Answers will vary, but variations 2 and 4 are generally preferred.

Experiment 14-2: PRODUCTION OF CARBON DIOXIDE USING BAKING POWDERS

1. A carbonate compound, usually sodium bicarbonate, and an acid.
2. The homemade baking powder.
3. Information in data table.
4. It had no effect on the pH.

Chapter 14: Leavening Agents and Baked Goods

LEAVENING AGENTS

TEXT PAGES 224–237

DIRECTIONS: What leavening agent was used to make each of these baked products? Fill in the blanks below.

Bread

Popover

Layer Cake

1. _____

2. _____

3. _____

Angel Food Cake

Banana Bread

Waffle

4. _____

5. _____

6. _____

Meringue Pie

Crackers

Biscuit

7. _____

8. _____

9. _____

CHAPTER
15

Fermentation and Food

TEXT PAGES 238–253

SUGGESTED TIME SCHEDULE

180-day course—9 days.
90-day course—4 days.

STUDENT OBJECTIVES

- Explain anaerobic respiration and how it is involved in both metabolism and food science.
- List three reasons why food is fermented.
- Identify bacteria used to ferment food.
- Compare fresh–pack pickling and brine pickling.
- Discuss how lactic acid bacteria create sauerkraut from cabbage.
- Describe the process of making vinegar.
- Identify the purposes of the ingredients used in making yeast breads.

CHAPTER SUMMARY

- Cell respiration is a multistep process that involves the breakdown of glucose and the release of energy.
- Anaerobic respiration, also called fermentation, is the first step in the breakdown of glucose and occurs without oxygen.
- Fermentation in food can be caused by bacteria, yeast, mold, and enzymes.
- Food can be fermented by lactic acid bacteria, acetic acid bacteria, carbon dioxide–producing bacteria, or proteolytic bacteria.
- Pickles can be made using either brine pickling or fresh–pack pickling methods.
- Yeast dough is a type of foam where bubbles of carbon dioxide produced by yeast are trapped in the dough by the starch and protein in flour.
- Yeast ferments grain and fruit to produce alcoholic beverages.

BACKGROUND INFORMATION

Chapter 15 explains the anaerobic fermentation used in producing pickled products, such as sauerkraut and yogurt. In addition, it describes the fermentation carried out by yeast in bread and beverage making.

Sanitation is of utmost importance in **Experiment 15-A: Fermentation of Pickles**. If students are not careful, they can introduce harmful bacteria into the pickles. These bacteria may compete with the lactic acid bacteria that are naturally present in cucumbers. This experiment illustrates that bacteria are everywhere, since lactic acid bacteria are not added to the cucumbers—they are naturally present on the vegetables used for fermentation.

If the pH rises above 4.5 during the fermentation of the pickles, do not allow students to taste the product. At that pH level, microbes that cause illness can grow and multiply.

Peanuts that are stored before processing can ferment, which causes them to become bitter. To prevent fermentation, peanut manufacturers now test the peanuts they receive for the by-products of fermentation.

Teacher's Resource Guide
REPRODUCIBLE MATERIALS

T-17:   The Process of Fermentation
E-15-A: Fermentation of Pickles

ACTIVITIES

1. Discuss fermentation and its role in the body and in food preparation. Use **T-17: The Process of Fermentation** to help students understand the chemical reactions that occur during fermentation. This is printed in the *Guide* and in the *Student Activity Workbook*.

2. Have students list fermented foods that they eat. How often do they eat these foods? Are fermented foods an important part of students' diets? Ask students to develop a list of as many foods as possible that are fermented. They may wish to survey a grocery store or cookbooks in compiling the list.

3. Discuss with students the role of fermentation in food preservation around the world. Are there other places where fermented foods are used more frequently than in students' diets? Less frequently?

4. Have students look through cookbooks for pickle and sauerkraut recipes. Do the recipes they locate use brine or fresh-pack methods of pickling? Students can compare the recipes and explain how differences among recipes would affect the fermentation process.

5. Obtain a Cooperative Extension Service bulletin on fermentation, pickling, or making sauerkraut. Discuss its contents with students.

6. In preparation for **Experiment 15-1: Yeast Fermentation**, demonstrate the procedures used in conducting the experiment. Explain that unless the container is closed tightly, the ginger ale will not become carbonated because the gas will escape.

7. Prepare apple cider as an additional demonstration of yeast fermentation in a beverage.

EXTENSION ACTIVITIES

1. Have students repeat **Experiment 15-2: Yeast Growth** using temperature as the variable. Suggested temperatures include 30°C, 35°C, 50°C, and 70°C. Use the ingredients from variation 2.

2. Have students perform **Experiment 15-A: Fermentation of Pickles**.

OVERVIEW OF EXPERIMENTS

● *Experiment 15-1:* YEAST FERMENTATION

Time Required

Day 1—30 minutes
Day 2—30 minutes
Day 4—10 minutes

Objective

Students will use yeast fermentation to produce ginger ale.

Equipment

- 12 400-mL beakers
- 12 thermometers
- 12 454-mL (1 pint) canning jars with lids
- 12 227-mL (8 oz) canning jars with lids
- 12 funnels
- 12 stirring rods
- heat source

Supplies

- 1 can/bottle ginger
- 1 small bottle, lime juice
- 500 g sugar
- 1 can/bottle cream of tartar
- 24 g baker's yeast
- filter paper
- pen or labels for labeling jars

Helpful Hints

- While one partner is heating the water, the other can be massing the solid ingredients and measuring the lime juice.

● *Experiment 15-2:* YEAST GROWTH

Time Required

45 minutes

Objective

Students will test various environments to determine which provides optimum conditions for yeast growth.

Equipment

- 12 100-mL graduated cylinders
- 12 250-mL beakers
- 12 laboratory thermometers
- 12 saucepans
- 12 metric rulers

Supplies

- dry yeast
- sucrose
- sodium chloride

Helpful Hints

- Draw a data table on the chalkboard so students can record their data on it for later averaging.
- If there is time, extend the 15-minute period during which the yeast are allowed to grow. A longer time will make the differences in growth easier to detect.

Laboratory Simplification

Do variations 1 and 2 only.

Laboratory Enrichment

Repeat lab at 45°C and 20°C.

Expected Data

Variation	Height	Odor	Consistency
1	2.8 cm	dough smell	runny/watery
2	3.5 cm	yeasty	foamy
3	3.0 cm	yeasty	watery
4	2.5 cm	dough smell	creamy

● *Experiment* 15-A: FERMENTATION OF PICKLES

Note: The procedure for this experiment is printed only in the *Teacher's Resource Guide*.

Time Required

Day 1—40 minutes
Daily checks—5 minutes

Objective

Students will prepare pickles and monitor their fermentation, observing changes in pH, color, texture, and appearance.

Equipment

- 12 wide-mouth 0.9-L jars and lids OR
- 12 1000-mL beakers
- 12 large knives
- 6 triple beam balances

Supplies

- 1 lug (flat) small cucumbers
- spices to taste
- sodium chloride
- 12 0.5-L plastic bags that seal
- pH indicator paper
- masking tape
- marking pen

Helpful Hints

- Prepare a brine solution by using 28.8 g salt per liter of solution. This brine is used to cover the pickles and to fill the plastic bags.
- Surfaces and utensils must be thoroughly cleaned before handling the cucumbers to prevent harmful bacteria from being introduced into the pickles.
- A variety of spices can be used to flavor the pickles, although you may prefer to use only dill.
- Have students wipe around the top of the cucumbers and the bottom of the brine-filled plastic bag each day.
- Every 3–4 days, have students do a "data check" to evaluate the pH, color, texture, and appearance of the cucumbers and brine. They should write their results in their data tables.
- The pH of the pickles may go up for a day or two before going down. It should stabilize between 3–3.5 in 4–5 weeks. If the pH goes higher than 4.5, discard the contents of the container.

ANSWER KEY

Student Text

● ANSWERS TO QUESTIONS IN TEXT:

p. 240

Wine is pasteurized to kill the bacteria that would otherwise spoil the wine by producing vinegar instead of alcohol.

p. 244

Indigenous bacteria are not used in making yogurt because it is impossible to know if the bacteria present in a given sample of milk are the best ones for making yogurt.

p. 245

Answers will vary.

p. 247

The dry method is used for producing about 60% of the world's coffee.

p. 250

1. Yogurt shows the greatest decrease in Vitamin A.
2. Sauerkraut shows the greatest increase in Riboflavin.

● CHECK YOUR FACTS

1. Fermentation or respiration that occurs in the absence of oxygen.
2. To preserve food, to improve the flavor of food, and to make food more palatable.
3. Yeast, bacteria, or mold.
4. They act on protein rather than carbohydrates.
5. Lactic acid bacteria.
6. It decreases.
7. Brine Pickling—the food being pickled ferments for several weeks in brine pickling, but fresh-pack pickling only takes a few days because flavor is added by vinegar and spices rather than the production of lactic acid.
8. They are killed as the pH decreases when lactic acid is produced during fermentation.
9. Acetic acid bacteria.
10. Proteolytic bacteria.
11. Because the bubbles of carbon dioxide are surrounded by the starch and protein of the dough.
12. Gluten.
13. It affects the amount of alcohol produced during fermentation.

● CRITICAL THINKING AND PROBLEM SOLVING

1. Anaerobic respiration is the first series of steps in the total process of cell respiration.
2. The heat would kill the indigenous bacteria that cause fermentation, so the cucumbers wouldn't pickle.
3. The milk used to make yogurt has been sterilized and therefore no longer contains indigenous bacteria. Adding bacteria allows yogurt makers more control over the quality of the final product.
4. The sugar in milk is lactose, the one sugar yeast cannot ferment.
5. Once the temperature of the dough rises to that of the oven, the yeast die and no longer produce carbon dioxide, so steam becomes more important as a leavener.
6. The bread would not rise properly because the extra salt would probably kill at least some of the yeast, and inhibit growth.
7. The limited sugar content would prevent yeast from producing an acceptable alcohol level.
8. The fermentation of wine is done by yeast, which are not killed during pasteurization.
9. The sugar present in the cider is fermented by yeast and becomes ethyl alcohol. Fermented cider is not as sweet as fresh cider and contains some alcohol.

Student Activity Workbook

● H-15-1: STUDY GUIDE

1. glucose	13. brine pickling
2. cell respiration	14. crisp (or firm)
3. aerobic	15. fresh-pack pickling
4. anaerobic	16. lactic acid
5. anaerobic respiration	17. indigenous
6. fermentation	18. acetic acid
7. microorganisms (or microbes)	19. Carbon dioxide
8. pasteurization	20. Proteolytic
9. lactic acid	21. lactose
10. lowered	22. gluten
11. 4.5	23. slow down
12. brine	24. dry
	25. sucrase

26. $C_6H_{12}O_6 \rightarrow 2HC_3H_5O_3 + Energy$
27. $C_6H_{12}O_6 \rightarrow 2C_2H_5OH + 2CO_2$

• H-15-2: SCRAMBLED WORDS

1. sauerkraut
2. fermentation
3. pickles
4. brine
5. fresh-pack
6. alcohol
7. yeast
8. energy
9. glucose
10. anaerobic
11. microorganisms
12. Pasteur
13. lactic acid
14. chocolate
15. coffee

• H-15-3: ANALOGIES

1. b
2. c
3. a
4. b
5. d
6. d
7. b
8. b
9. b
10. d

• H-15-4: NUTRITION AND YOU

1. Water soluble vitamins dissolve in the brine and therefore are lost during pickling.
2. The energy lost by food during fermentation may be used by the bacteria that cause fermentation.
3. Some foods are more nutritious after fermentation because the microorganisms that cause fermentation may produce Vitamin B_{12} and riboflavin.
4. Fat-soluble vitamins are usually not changed by fermentation.
5. Cucumbers are more nutritious since they are lower in kilocalories yet higher in Vitamins A and C.
6. Yogurt shows the greatest increase in calcium content.
7. Yogurt shows the greatest decrease in Vitamin A.
8. Yogurt provides much more calcium per serving than milk.
9. The decrease in Vitamin A is the greatest nutritional loss between milk and yogurt.
10. Answers will vary.

• T-17: THE PROCESS OF FERMENTATION

1. Glucose, lactic acid
2. Glucose, Ethyl alcohol, Carbon dioxide
   Ethyl alcohol, Oxygen, Acetic acid, Water
3. Glucose, Ethyl alcohol, Carbon dioxide

• Experiment 15-1: YEAST FERMENTATION

1. Bubbles should begin to appear within minutes of adding the yeast to the mixture.
2. Carbonation will probably be at a maximum on the second day (when the students first open the canning jar after it has been left overnight). The solution tends to go fairly flat during the time that the filtering is taking place.
3. The bubbles are carbon dioxide gas.

• Experiment 15-2: YEAST GROWTH

1. The yeast grow best in variation 2, because of the added sugar. It grew most slowly in variation 4 because of the added salt and sugar.
2. The heat would have killed the yeast.
3. Answers will vary.

Teacher's Resource Guide

• Experiment 15-A: FERMENTATION OF PICKLES

1. Information in data table.
2. Information in data table.
3. Answers will vary, but the final pH should be 3–3.5.
4. If the pH is in the above range, it is low enough to preserve the pickles. If the pH is higher, wine vinegar could be added (which would affect the flavor), and the pickles fermented a few more days to see if they reach an acceptable pH level. Otherwise, the sample should be discarded.

Chapter 15: Fermentation and Food

THE PROCESS OF FERMENTATION

TEXT PAGES 238–253

DIRECTIONS: Fermentation is a chemical reaction that splits complex organic compounds into relatively simpler substances. Identify the common name for the molecules shown.

1. IN LACTIC ACID FERMENTATION

lactic acid
bacteria

$$C_6H_{12}O_6 \longrightarrow 2HC_3H_5O_3 + Energy$$

_____   _____

_____

2. IN ACETIC ACID FERMENTATION (a two-step process)

yeast

$$1.\ C_6H_{12}O_6 \longrightarrow 2C_2H_5OH \quad + \quad 2CO_2$$

_____   _____   _____

_____   _____

acetic acid
bacteria

$$2.\ C_2H_5OH \quad + \quad O_2 \longrightarrow CH_3COOH \quad + \quad H_2O$$

_____   _____   _____   _____

_____

3. IN YEAST FERMENTATION

yeast

$$C_6H_{12}O_6 \longrightarrow 2C_2H_5OH \quad + \quad 2CO_2$$

_____   _____   _____

_____   _____

SAFETY: Place your initials under each appropriate symbol to show the safety precautions you need to remember when performing this experiment.

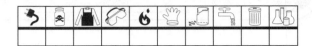

In this experiment, you will prepare pickles from cucumbers. As the fermentation process proceeds, you will monitor changes in color and texture of the cucumbers and appearance and pH of the brine.

PROCEDURE

1. Thoroughly wash a beaker. Label with your name and class period.
2. Wash 4–6 cucumbers.
3. Mass 2 g pickling spice and 2 g dill seed. Pour the spice and dill seed into the beaker.
4. Put the washed cucumbers into the beaker.
5. Add brine supplied by your teacher until the pickles are completely covered.
6. Fill a plastic bag with brine solution and seal tightly. Place the plastic bag on top of the cucumbers to submerge them in the brine.
7. Leave your beaker in the location indicated by your teacher.
8. Every few days:

   a. Check to see that the cucumbers are covered with liquid. If necessary, add more brine.
   b. Skim off any film that may form.
   c. Record the following information in your data table: color of the cucumber/pickles; texture of the cucumbers/pickles; appearance of the brine (clear, cloudy); and pH of the brine as tested with pH paper.

9. Allow the fermentation process to continue for about 5 weeks or until the pH of the brine stabilizes at 3.5 or below for at least a week. Do not taste the pickles if the pH remains above 4.

QUESTIONS

1. What changes occurred in the color and texture of the cucumbers as they fermented?
2. What changes occurred in the appearance of the brine as the cucumbers fermented?
3. What is the final pH of the brine solution?
4. Is the pH low enough to preserve the pickles? If not, what could you do about it?

SAMPLE DATA TABLE

Date	Color	Texture	Brine Appearance	Brine pH

CHAPTER

16

Dairy Products and Processing

TEXT PAGES 254-271

SUGGESTED TIME SCHEDULE

180-day course—8 days.
90-day course—4 days.

STUDENT OBJECTIVES

- List the components of milk and explain how each is dispersed in the milk.
- Describe what happens when milk protein is coagulated.
- Discuss the processing of milk and how it is treated when it is pasteurized, homogenized, and fortified.
- Compare and contrast skim milk, low–fat milk, whole milk, half–and–half, and various creams.
- Differentiate between evaporated milk, condensed milk, and dried milk.
- Identify factors that affect the ability of cream to form a foam.
- Explain the changes that occur when milk is heated.
- Describe the process of making a fermented or cultured milk product and list examples of these products.

CHAPTER SUMMARY

- Milk and milk products are sources of protein, fat, carbohydrate, vitamins, and minerals.
- Milk is a complex product that has substances in solution, in colloidal dispersions, and in emulsions.
- Lactose intolerance results from the absence of lactase in the intestine to digest the lactose in milk.
- Milk is pasteurized, homogenized, and fortified during processing.
- Fresh fluid milk products are classified according to fat content.
- The ability of cream to form a foam depends on the fat content of the cream, the temperature, the amount of cream, and the point at which sugar is added.
- Heat denatures and coagulates the protein in milk and can cause the milk to curdle.
- Fermented milk products are commercially made from pasteurized milk inoculated with specific starter cultures, which produce the desired flavor or texture.

BACKGROUND INFORMATION

Chapter 16 focuses on the composition and properties of cow's milk. The chapter discusses milk processing, cooking with milk, and how fermentation is used as means of preserving milk.

Milk and milk products are one of the primary sources of calcium in the diet. However, various milk products differ greatly in the amounts of calcium they contain. For example:
- 240 mL skim milk contains 300 mg calcium.
- 240 mL plain yogurt contains 400 mg calcium.
- 240 mL cottage cheese contains 150 mg calcium.
- 240 mL ice cream contains 170 mg calcium.

Lactose intolerance is present in about 30 percent of the population in the United States. It is now possible to buy the enzyme lactase in tablet form. This means a person with lactose intolerance can take a tablet to help break down lactose after drinking milk or eating a milk product.

Yogurt varies in the number of calories present in an average serving. Flavored yogurt made from whole milk may contain as many as 390 calories in a 228 g serving, while plain low–fat yogurt may contain as few as 90 calories in a 228 g serving. Encourage students to read the labels on yogurt containers so they will know how many kilocalories they are consuming when eating yogurt.

REPRODUCIBLE MATERIALS

T-18:   Storage Life of Dairy Products

ACTIVITIES

1. Discuss with students the composition of milk and its importance in the diet. How much milk do students drink each day? What milk products do they eat regularly?
2. Review the techniques used to process milk. What is the purpose of each? How is the purpose accomplished?
3. Have students tour a commercial dairy to observe the processing techniques discussed in Activity 2.
4. Show the film: "Food for Thought: Milk and Milk Products," BECF, 1982 (12 minutes).
5. Show the class examples of buttermilk and evaporated, condensed, and dried milk so students can see how the samples vary in color and viscosity.
6. Show the class samples of very hard, hard, semi-soft, and soft cheeses. Have students sample the cheeses to experience the differences in mouthfeel. Discuss how the amount of water present affects the shelf life of a cheese.
7. Divide students into small groups to read and present oral reports on the following articles:
   - "The Secret of Roquefort: Milk, Mold, and Method," *Smithsonian*, February 1983, page 56.
   - Anne Mendelson, "A Touch of Culture," *Cuisine*, April 1981, page 42.
   - "Brie and Mexican Cheese Recall," FDA *Consumer*, May 1986, page 4.
   - Chris Lecos, "A Closer Look at Dairy Safety," FDA *Consumer*, April 1986, page 14.
   - Carmen Brining, "The Lactose Dilemma," *Saturday Evening Post*, September 1987, page 66.
   - "Buying Guide for Yogurt," *University of California at Berkeley Wellness Letter*, June 1987, page 3.
8. Use **T-18: Storage Life of Dairy Products**. This is printed in the *Guide* and in the *Student Activity Workbook*.

OVERVIEW OF EXPERIMENTS

● *Experiment 16-1:* MAKING YOGURT

Time Required

Day 1—45 minutes
Day 2—20 minutes

Objective

Students will prepare yogurt using three yogurt bases and will compare the color, texture, taste, aftertaste, and pH of the final products.

Equipment

- 12 50-mL beakers
- 12 ring stands and clamps
- 12 small saucepans or double boilers
- 12 square baking pans
- 12 laboratory thermometers in stoppers
- 24 custard cups or yogurt containers
- incubators or yogurt makers (optional)

Supplies

- 1.9 L 1 percent milk
- 1.9 L 2 percent milk
- 1.9 L skim milk
- 0.5 L plain yogurt for active starter bacteria

Helpful Hints

- Second-hand stores often sell used yogurt makers at low prices. These are much easier to use than an oven. If yogurt makers are not available, incubators, which will produce excellent yogurt, can be set at 43°C. Some food dehydrators can be used to maintain an environment of 43°C.
- If you ferment the yogurt in the oven, use the "setting pan" apparatus. Have students place the filled custard cups in the square baking pan. Hot water is poured into the pan so that the water level in the pan is above the yogurt level in the cups. Be sure no water splashes into the yogurt cups. The setting pan is then placed in the oven.
- The yogurt bases should be labeled with three-digit numbers to avoid influencing student responses to the yogurt produced. For the data below: 476 = 2 percent milk, 539 = skim milk, and 168 = 1 percent milk.

- Prior to the experiment, discuss the importance of sanitation. Undesirable bacteria can easily be introduced into the yogurt. In addition, stress the importance of temperature control. Too high a temperature will kill the lactic acid bacteria, and too low a temperature will slow their growth.
- Check the label to make sure that the plain yogurt purchased for the starter contains "live" bacteria.
- Give each laboratory group 200 mL milk to use as the yogurt base.
- Students can use a 50-mL beaker to carry the 30 mL yogurt starter from a central location to their laboratory stations.
- Generally, if the last class of the day ends by 4:00 p.m., the yogurt will be ready to be transferred to the refrigerator by 10:00 p.m. Place it on labeled trays, one for each class. If it is impossible for you to enter the school building in the evening, the yogurt can be left overnight in the yogurt maker or oven, but the quality will not be as good.

Laboratory Simplification

None.

Laboratory Enrichment

Make yogurt cheese. See *Sunset*, April 1980, page 117.

Expected Data

Yogurt Base	pH	Color	Texture	Taste/Aftertaste
476	3.5	white	smooth	pleasant
539	2.5	yellow	grainy	slightly bitter
168	3.0	creamy	grainy	bitter

● *Experiment* 16-2: EVALUATION OF COMMERCIAL YOGURTS

Time Required

30 minutes

Objective

Students will use their knowledge of sensory evaluation to evaluate commercial yogurts for color, texture, and taste.

Equipment

- 7 saucers or small plates
- 7 serving spoons
- 24 teaspoons
- 24 small water glasses

Supplies

- 24 small paper plates
- 7 228-g containers of flavored yogurt
- 24 28-mL paper cups (instead of water glasses)
- masking tape
- marking pen

Helpful Hints

- It is best to select one flavor of yogurt and buy several brands of that flavor, e.g., seven samples of strawberry or seven samples of raspberry.
- Before students enter the classroom, empty the contents of each yogurt container on a saucer and label the plate with a triple-digit number. Be sure to keep a master list so you will know which number corresponds to which brand.
- Wash and dry the containers so students can use them later to gain information about the different brands of yogurt. It is a good idea to save the yogurt containers for future experiments, so that more are available for student use when answering the experiment questions.
- Place serving spoons and the plates containing the yogurt at seven stations around the classroom. Each student should get a small plate and place a bite-sized sample of each yogurt on the plate. Paper plates work best because students can write the sample number on the plate next to each sample. Students should rinse their mouths with water after tasting each sample.
- After students have tasted all the brands available, provide brand and unit cost information for each sample used in the experiment.

Laboratory Simplification

None.

Laboratory Enrichment

After students have completed the experiment, have them add flavors to the yogurt base they liked best. Students can add artificial flavors or fresh fruit and then evaluate the flavored product. Commercially prepared plain yogurt can also be used for student experimentation with flavorings.

Expected Data

Results will vary, depending on the brands available and the personal preferences of students.

ANSWER KEY
Student Text

● ANSWERS TO QUESTIONS IN TEXT:

p. 255

The sugar found in milk is lactose.

p. 260

An opaque container is preferred over a clear container for the storage of milk in order to prevent the loss of riboflavin which is destroyed by light.

p. 261

Milk is considered a good source of protein because it contains all the essential amino acids needed by humans. The most important mineral found in milk is calcium. This is because the calcium found in milk is readily used by the body.

p. 266

Milk is heated when making yogurt in order to kill unwanted bacteria and to denature the whey proteins.

● CHECK YOUR FACTS

1. Casein and whey.
2. The light reflected from the more or less spherical micelles found in milk.
3. Casein.
4. By homogenizing milk.
5. It provides energy, makes milk sweet, provides a substrate for the formation of lactic acid, and adds body to milk.
6. Riboflavin, thiamin, niacin, and vitamin A. Vitamin D is added during processing.
7. To test for pasteurization.

8. The cream has been pasteurized at ultra-high temperatures for a short time.
9. Room temperatures cause the rapid growth of bacteria that hasten spoilage.
10. The amount of fat they contain. Skim milk has none, whole milk has 3.5 percent, and coffee cream has 18 percent.
11. Condensed milk has added sugar.
12. After the desired volume and stiffness have been reached, since adding it earlier increases the whipping time and decreases the volume and stiffness of the foam.
13. Select and prepare a starter culture, pasteurize the milk, add the starter to the milk, allow the culture to grow, agitate the product, and cool it to slow the bacterial growth.
14. Ripened cheeses have been stored for at least 60 days while chemical changes occur in the cheeses. Examples are Cheddar and Romano. Unripened cheeses are eaten fresh within a few weeks. Examples are cottage and cream.

● CRITICAL THINKING AND PROBLEM SOLVING

1. Water, the solvent in milk, contains many particles. Some dissolve to form solutions, some are so large they form colloidal dispersions, and the fat forms an emulsion.
2. No—it contains relatively little cholesterol, especially if low-fat or skim milk is used. It is important to drink milk for its vitamins and minerals.
3. People with a lactose intolerance—so they can drink milk and eat milk products without side effects.
4. Curds and whey—curdled milk. The curds are coagulated casein, and the whey is the liquid that remains after curdling.
5. Milk that has been pasteurized has been heated to high temperatures to kill bacteria present in the milk. Milk that has been homogenized has been forced through small openings under pressure to break down the fat particles to a size that will remain uniformly distributed in the milk. Milk that has been fortified has had vitamin D added.
6. The light that goes through the glass could destroy the riboflavin in the milk.
7. The air leaves the foam if it stands too long.
8. It decreases because the nutrients trapped in the skin are removed.

9. To kill any unwanted bacteria and denature the whey protein.
10. Fermented products because they are too acidic for spoilage bacteria to grow, and canned products because they have been sterilized to kill the bacteria and no new bacteria can enter the sealed cans.

Student Activity Workbook

● H-16-1: STUDY GUIDE

1. cow's
2. 87
3. fat (and water)
4. casein
5. micelles
6. light
7. acids
8. curdled
9. serum
10. heat
11. denatured
12. 20
13. creaming
14. lactose
15. lactase
16. lactose intolerance
17. riboflavin
18. vitamin D
19. complete
20. calcium
21. shelf life
22. UHT
23. fat
24. 35
25. Carrageenin
26. 44
27. increases
28. cold
29. decreases
30. precipitate
31. casein
32. starter
33. hard

● H-16-2: SECRET WORD

1. evaporated
2. carrageenin
3. casein
4. buttermilk
5. whey
6. inoculation
7. fortified
8. micelles
9. homogenization
10. phosphatase
11. starter
12. skim
13. riboflavin
14. creaming

The secret word is pasteurization.

● H-16-3: NUTRITION AND YOU

1. essential
2. milk
3. calcium, phosphorus, magnesium, zinc
4. calcium
5. phosphorus
6. Riboflavin, thiamin, niacin
7. small
8. cheese
9. cream, butter
10. c

● T-18: STORAGE LIFE OF DAIRY PRODUCTS

1. -23°C, 10°C
2. 4°C, -1°C
3. 4°C, 1°C
4. 4°C, 43°C
5. 4°C, Above 38°C
6. 21°C

● Experiment 16-1: MAKING YOGURT

1. The yogurt made from 2 percent milk (base 476) had the most appetizing color.
2. Yes—the 2 percent milk (base 476) produced the only smooth yogurt.
3. The 1 percent milk (base 168) produced yogurt with a bitter taste, while skim milk (base 539) produced a slightly bitter-tasting yogurt.
4. Skim milk (base 539) produced the most acidic yogurt.
5. Yes—the sample with the best flavor had the least acidic pH.
6. The 2 percent milk (base 476) seemed to produce the best yogurt.
7. Answers will vary.

● Experiment 16-2: EVALUATION OF COMMERCIAL YOGURTS

Answers to all questions will vary depending on the brands of yogurt tested. If you compile the answers the first time students conduct the experiment and use the same brands in later years, you will have the answers to refer to when repeating the experiment.

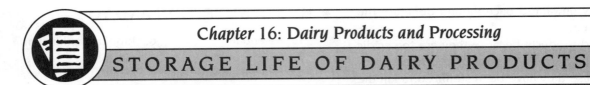

STORAGE LIFE OF DAIRY PRODUCTS

TEXT PAGES 254-271

DIRECTIONS: Fill in the temperatures below.

Product	Approximate Storage Life at Specific Temperatures	Critical or Dangerous Storage Conditions
1. Butter	1 month at 4°C 12 months at _____	Above _____ or damp or wet storage
2. Cheddar Cheese	6 months at _____ 18 months at 1°C	Above 16°C or below _____
3. Processed Cheese	3 months at 21°C 12 months at _____	Above 32°C or below _____
4. Nonfat dry milk	6 months at 32°C 16 months at 21°C 24 months at _____	Above _____
5. Condensed milk	3 months at 32°C 9 months at 21°C 15 months at _____	_____ _____ or below -1°C, or dampness to cause can rusting
6. Evaporated milk	1 month at 32°C 12 months at _____ 24 months at 4°C	Above 32°C or below -1°C, or dampness to cause can rusting

TEXT PAGES 274-289

SUGGESTED TIME SCHEDULE

180-day course—9 days.
90-day course—4 days.

STUDENT OBJECTIVES

- Name and describe the properties of the microorganisms that cause food spoilage.
- Differentiate between food intoxication and food infection.
- List specific organisms that can cause foodborne illness.
- Discuss sanitary and food–handling practices that can help prevent food poisoning.
- Identify United States government agencies that keep the food supply safe.
- Describe information required on a food label.

CHAPTER SUMMARY

- Mold, yeast, bacteria, and enzymes can cause physical and chemical changes in food, which make it unappetizing and possibly dangerous to eat.
- Foodborne illness can be caused by toxic chemicals, toxins produced by microorganisms, pathogenic microorganisms, and animal parasites or their eggs.
- *Clostridium perfringens*, *Staphylococcus aureus*, and *Clostridium botulinum* are bacteria that produce toxins that cause food intoxication.
- The major cause of food infection is the bacteria called *Salmonella*.
- Food poisoning can be prevented by proper sanitary and food–handling practices.
- The Food and Drug Administration is the federal agency responsible for monitoring the general food supply.
- The GRAS list includes over 600 ingredients generally recognized as safe in food.
- The information required on food labels is strictly regulated by law.

BACKGROUND INFORMATION

After a discussion of foodborne illness and the microorganisms that cause it, Chapter 17 describes ways of preventing food poisoning in the laboratory and at home. The role of the United States federal government in protecting consumers from unsafe food is also discussed.

All foods begin to break down from the moment of ripeness or from the point when they are picked. Post–harvest food scientists are constantly trying to find ways to stop or slow down the process of degradation.

This chapter can be incorporated into the curriculum sooner in the year, if necessary. Some students benefit from an early exposure to the need for cleanliness and good sanitation habits.

Because proper food handling is so important in preventing foodborne illness, stress the importance of keeping food either very hot or very cold. The temperature range between 4°–60°C is often called the danger zone because most bacteria grow very quickly within this temperature range.

Emphasize the importance of washing one's hands, not only in the foods laboratory but as a daily habit. Most bacteria and viruses, including those causing the common cold, are now thought to be spread by hand–to–hand contact, rather than by inhalation. A 30–second washing can rid the hands of up to 90 percent of the particles that may carry viruses.

In discussing the importance of hand washing, remind students to avoid recontaminating the hands after washing. When washing one's hands in a public restroom, turn on the water, wash hands thoroughly with soap, rinse, take a paper towel, and use it to turn off the faucet, dry the hands, and open the door. Because many people do not wash their hands, their germs are on the faucets and door handles.

Teacher's Resource Guide
REPRODUCIBLE MATERIALS

T-1 :   Keeping Food Safe to Eat

ACTIVITIES

1. Show the film: "Key to Cleanliness," IFBI, 1983 (21 minutes). This film on sanitation provides an excellent overview to begin the chapter.
2. Discuss with students the various microorganisms that spoil food, focusing on the bacteria that can cause foodborne illness. Differentiate between food intoxication and food infection.
3. Use **T-19: Keeping Food Safe to Eat** to introduce students to safe food handling and sanitation techniques for keeping food safe. It is printed in the *Guide* and in the *Student Activity Workbook*. What other ways can students think of to promote food safety?
4. Have students read and discuss some or all of the following articles:
   - "What Is Poisoning All These People?" *Good Housekeeping*, May 1986, page 113.
   - "Brie and Mexican Cheese Recalled," FDA *Consumer*, May 1986, page 4.
   - "Botulism," FDA *Consumer Magazine*, April 1986, page 36.
   - "FDA Food Safety Watch," *Tufts University Diet and Nutrition Newsletter*, March 1986.
   - "It Must Have Been Something You Ate," *Discover Magazine*, February 1987, page 94.
   - Earl Mindell, "Unsafe Food, How to Spot It and How to Prevent It," *Family Circle*, April 14, 1987, page 68.
   - "Summer Food Safety Tips," FDA *Consumer*, June 1987, page 17.
5. Discuss with students the various United States government agencies involved in monitoring the food supply.
6. Invite a state food inspector or someone from the local or state Public Health Department to talk with students about the government's regulation of food safety.
7. Have students read and discuss the following article: "Nutrition Labeling and Health Claims," *Dairy Council Digest*, December 1986, page 31.
8. Have students read and discuss the following article: "Making a Date with Food Freshness," *Current Health*, May 1986. In a study of garbage done at Oregon State University, it was found that most families do not understand the dating of food. As a result, they throw away much food that would still be good for another week.
9. Have students look at various food labels to see what information can be found on the labels. What information is common to all the labels? What information is found only on some labels? Why don't all labels contain the same information?
10. In preparation for **Experiment 17-1: Growing Cultures**, demonstrate the techniques of marking the Petri dish and taking the samples with the cellophane tape.

OVERVIEW OF EXPERIMENTS

- ### Experiment 17-1: GROWING CULTURES

Time Required

Day 1—30 minutes
Days 2, 3, 4, 5—5 minutes each day.

Objective

Students will grow cultures which demonstrate the presence of bacteria on unwashed surfaces.

Equipment

- 12 sterile Petri dishes

Supplies

- agar (see below)
- cellophane tape
- marking pen
- masking tape

Helpful Hints

- It is possible to buy disposable Petri dishes prefilled with agar. These can be a real timesaver. Check with the biology department at your school.

- If you decide to prepare the agar yourself, add 15 g agar to 1000 mL water, heat to boiling to completely dissolve the agar, then pour the boiling mixture into sterile Petri dishes. The dishes hold 50–60 mL each, so 1000 mL of agar is enough for a class set.
- After students have placed their samples on the agar, place the Petri dishes on a tray marked with the class period. Place the tray on top of the refrigerator. It will be out of the way and the warm surface will encourage bacterial growth.

Laboratory Simplification

None.

Laboratory Enrichment

Students repeat the experiment at home in their kitchens.

Expected Data

Data will vary greatly, but in general, any unwashed surface is likely to produce one or more types of bacteria. As long as the tape is a reasonably new roll, the section of the agar touched only by clean tape should remain free of bacterial growth.

● Experiment 17-2: BACTERIA IN MILK

Time Required

Day 1—15 minutes
Day 2—10 minutes

Objective

Students will compare the bacteria populations in fresh and week-old samples of raw and pasteurized milk.

Equipment

- 48 test tubes
- 12 10-mL graduated cylinders
- 12 stirring rods
- 12 250-mL beakers
- food dehydrator or incubator

Supplies

- 1 L fresh raw milk
- 1 L week-old raw milk
- 1 L fresh pasteurized milk
- 1 L week-old pasteurized milk
- masking tape
- labels
- methylene blue

Helpful Hints

- It is easiest to purchase methylene blue solution. The concentration of such solutions may vary depending on the source. If you have a solution of 1:20,000 methylene blue, use 0.5 mL per 10 mL milk. The amount of methylene blue should be adjusted if a different concentration is used.

Laboratory Simplification

None.

Laboratory Enrichment

Repeat experiment with samples left at room temperature for 24 hours.

Expected Data

Results will vary somewhat depending on the exact age of the milk samples and the handling of the raw milk.

Test Tube	Time Required to Decolorize Methylene Blue
1	1.5 hours
2	about 24 hours
3	20 minutes
4	about 8 hours

ANSWER KEY

Student Text

● ANSWERS TO QUESTIONS IN TEXT:

p. 277
1. Fruits and vegetables that have been picked at their prime have the greatest nutritional value.
2. If frozen food was processed immediately after harvesting, its nutritional value could be higher than fresh food that has been kept at room temperature for several days.

p. 278

Pesticide residues are a concern to the FDA because they may be toxic to humans.

p. 282

Steps that can help prevent food poisoning are: washing your hands before touching food, using only clean containers and utensils, using soap and water to wash all surfaces before and after use, and not allowing liquid from raw meat to drip on other food.

p. 284

The FAO was formed to eliminate hunger and improve nutrition worldwide.

● CHECK YOUR FACTS

1. Mold, yeast, bacteria, and enzymes.
2. Toxic chemicals, toxins produced by microorganisms, pathogenic microorganisms, and animal parasites or their eggs.
3. Food intoxication and food infection.
4. *Clostridium botulinium*, *Staphylococcus aureus*, *Clostridium perfringens*, and *Salmonella*.
5. When high-protein foods are kept warm for long periods of time before they are consumed.
6. Keeping perishable foods either very cold or very hot.
7. Botulism—it can be fatal.
8. *Salmonella*.
9. Sterilized with hot soapy water containing one part chlorine bleach to eight parts water both before and after cutting the raw meat.
10. It tastes exactly the same as uncontaminated food.
11. The Food and Drug Administration, the United States Department of Agriculture, and the Environmental Protection Agency.
12. A list of common ingredients that are Generally Recognized as Safe by the FDA.
13. Prior to the passage of the law, many foreign substances were added to food without consumers knowing it.

● CRITICAL THINKING AND PROBLEM SOLVING

1. Mold is often used in making cheese so there may be some left in the cheese. Mold can grow in the low temperatures in the refrigerator.
2. No—they need moisture to grow.

3. Food intoxication is caused by the toxins produced by microorganisms while food infections are caused by the microorganisms themselves.
4. These bacteria are always present in the intestinal tract.
5. When liquid from uncooked meat is allowed to drip on other food or when a food sample is placed in a container that has not been washed since another food sample was removed from it. (Examples may vary.)
6. It should be stored in a closed container in an ice chest until people are ready to eat. While people are serving themselves, the egg salad should not be sitting in the sun and, ideally, should sit in a dish of ice. As soon as people are finished serving themselves, any remaining egg salad should be covered and returned to the ice chest.
7. The cooked beef stew. It is an ideal place for the growth of C. *perfringens*.
8. The foods on it are safe to use without being considered additives.
9. Answers will vary.

Student Activity Workbook

● H-17-1: STUDY GUIDE

1. aerobic	16. *Salmonella*
2. 4–6.5	17. Cross contamination
3. sugar levels	18. raw pork
4. 100°C	19. 77°C
5. 20°C–50°C	20. 60
6. highest	21. 4 or less
7. foodborne illnesses	22. World Health Organization
8. pathogenic	23. poultry
9. toxins	24. Food and Drug Administration
10. pesticides	25. mercury
11. *Clostridium perfringens*	26. additive
12. stomach flu or virus	27. GRAS
13. meat	28. adulterated
14. improperly home-canned food	29. label
15. food infection	30. quantity

● H-17-2: CROSSWORD PUZZLE

Across
2. *Salmonella*
4. infection
7. FAO
8. intoxication
10. GRAS
12. flies
14. spore
16. safe
17. microorganisms

Down
1. *perfringens*
3. WHO
5. contamination
6. pathogenic
8. illness
9. toxin
11. additive
12. FDA
13. diarrhea
15. parasite

● H-17-3: ANALOGIES

1. a
2. b
3. d
4. d
5. a
6. b
7. d
8. c
9. b
10. c

● H-17-4: NUTRITION AND YOU

1. Fruits and vegetables that have been picked at their prime have the greatest nutritional value.
2. The nutritional value of produce steadily decreases as time passes.
3. Causes of food deterioration include light, high and low temperature, enzymes, radiation, dry air, microorganisms, industrial contaminants, insects, parasites, rodents, and oxygen in the air.
4. If produce partially freezes during shipment or storage, it may be inedible after it thaws.
5. Meats, milk and leafy vegetables can become unfit for human consumption if stored at room temperature for more than two days. This will happen even more quickly if the weather is warm.
6. Perishable cooked food becomes unsafe to eat if left at room temperature for more than two or three hours.
7. Rodents can spread disease carrying bacteria and viruses on food with which they make contact.

8. Dry cereal would retain its nutritional value longer at room temperature.
9. If frozen food was processed immediately after harvesting, its nutritional value could be higher than fresh food that has been kept at room temperature for several days.
10. milk—refrigerator
    eggs—refrigerator
    potato chips—at room temperature in a light-proof package
    strawberries—refrigerator
    bananas—room temperature
    flour—closed container at room temperature

● T-19: KEEPING FOOD SAFE TO EAT

1. clean
2. promptly
3. raw meat
4. hot
5. Sterilize
6. Wash hands
7. pesticides
8. thoroughly
9. cross
10. cold

● *Experiment 17-1: GROWING CULTURES*

1. Answers will vary—if no growth appeared on the agar, the tape was free of microorganisms.
2. Answers will vary—surfaces that show no growth on the agar were free of microorganisms.
3. Answers will vary.
4. By washing all surfaces and utensils that come in contact with food, washing hands before handling food, and rewashing hands after touching hair or clothing while working with food.

● *Experiment 17-2: BACTERIA IN MILK*

1. The fresh pasteurized milk had the fewest bacteria present while the raw week-old milk had the most present.
2. Pasteurization is important in producing milk that is safe to drink.
3. Pasteurize milk before it is distributed and keep it refrigerated.

Chapter 17: Food Safety

KEEPING FOOD SAFE TO EAT

T E X T   P A G E S   2 7 4 - 2 8 9

DIRECTIONS: Fill in the blanks in each sentence below.

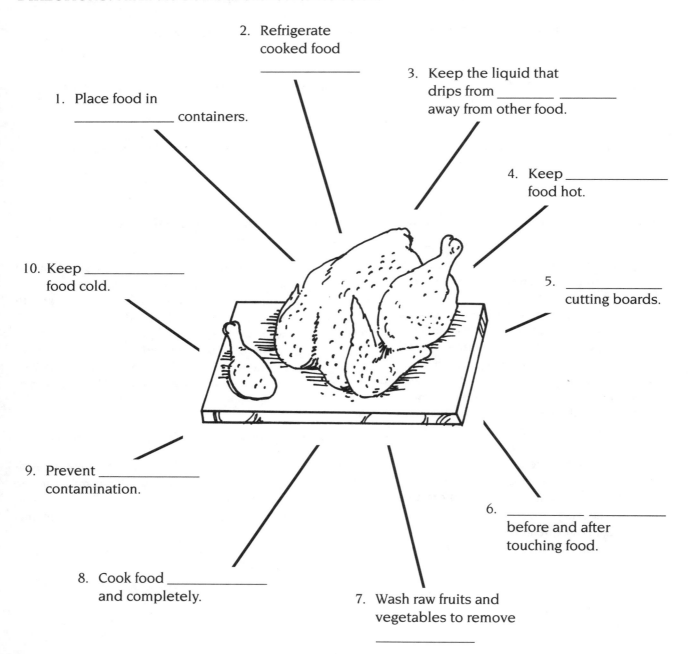

2. Refrigerate cooked food _____

3. Keep the liquid that drips from _____ _____ away from other food.

1. Place food in _____ containers.

4. Keep _____ food hot.

10. Keep _____ food cold.

5. _____ cutting boards.

9. Prevent _____ contamination.

6. _____ _____ before and after touching food.

8. Cook food _____ and completely.

7. Wash raw fruits and vegetables to remove _____

CHAPTER

18

Dehydration

TEXT PAGES 290–303

SUGGESTED TIME SCHEDULE

180-day course—6 days.
90-day course—4 days.

STUDENT OBJECTIVES

- List the purposes of dehydration.
- Explain why food is pretreated before dehydrating.
- Compare and contrast sulfiting, sulfuring, and blanching.
- Describe the different types of blanching that can be used as pretreatment methods.
- Discuss why air temperature and movement play an important role in successful dehydration.
- Identify four methods of dehydration and explain how they are similar and different.
- Describe how dried food should be stored.

CHAPTER SUMMARY

- Dehydration is a preservation method that removes water from food.
- Dehydration preserves food, decreases its weight and bulk for transport, and provides convenience in food preparation.
- Food is prepared for drying by being sorted for quality, sliced, and pretreated.
- Pretreatment by sulfiting, sulfuring, or blanching reduces flavor loss, enzymatic browning, and deterioration during storage.
- Air temperatures that are too high can cause case-hardening, while lack of air circulation prevents complete dehydration.
- Dehydration at home can be done by the sun, in an oven or room, or in a dehydrator.
- A dehydrator produces the best home-dried food because it provides a sanitary and consistent environment.
- Dried food should be stored in airtight containers to prevent moisture from reentering the food.

BACKGROUND INFORMATION

Chapter 18 presents information on dehydration, a common method of preserving food. While dehydration can be used with many types of foods, this chapter focuses on dehydrating fruits and vegetables. The basic purpose of drying food is to remove moisture so organisms that can spoil food will not grow while the food is stored.

Most people use the terms dehydrating and drying interchangeably, a practice followed in *Food Science*. Technically, the U.S. Department of Agriculture defines dehydrated foods as those that contain 2.5–4 percent residual moisture. Dried foods are those which contain between 10–20 percent moisture. Household dehydrators ordinarily produce foods with the higher level of moisture.

Dried food needs to be stored so it is not exposed to humidity, light, or air. Otherwise, the quality of the food and the length of storage time are adversely affected.

It is possible to use a microwave oven to dehydrate some spices. Generally, however, the microwave is not considered suitable for dehydration. Many manufacturers of convection ovens offer dehydrating trays. If these are used properly, they can produce acceptable dried products.

Food should not be dried over a floor heating vent. Too much dust circulates and ends up in the food. Fumes can sometimes cause combustion.

T-20:   Dehydration/Rehydration
E-18-A: Making Raisins

ACTIVITIES

1. Obtain samples of several foods in dehydrated and fresh forms. Examples could include grapes and raisins; fresh and dried peaches, pears, apricots, or apples; reconstituted and freshly made mashed potatoes; or fresh and reconstituted (from powder) lemonade. Have students evaluate the products for their sensory qualities and determine what the effects of dehydration (or dehydration/ rehydration) are on the quality of the foods.

2. Discuss with students the long history of dehydration as a means of food preservation. Review both home and commercial methods of dehydration.

3. Show students different types of dehydrators. Obtain a book on drying food that has illustrations and guidelines on building dehydrators. Using the book, explain that it is possible to build a home dehydrator. Encourage any interested student to pursue such a project.

4. Demonstrate drying foods other than fruits and vegetables. Possibilities could include nuts or meat jerky.

5. Have students examine and test various types of containers that could be used for storing dried food. What container would be the best choice? Why?

6. Prepare dried beans that have been soaked overnight and those that have not been soaked. Have students sample and evaluate the beans.

7. Have students read and discuss the following article: "An Order of Fries—Hold the Sulfites," FDA *Consumer*, March 1988, page 9.

8. Use **T-20: Dehydration/Rehydration** to summarize for students the effect dehydration and rehydration had on water loss and gain during the two experiments in this chapter. It is printed in the *Guide* and in the *Student Activity Workbook*.

EXTENSION ACTIVITY

Have students conduct **Experiment 18-A: Making Raisins** in the classroom or at home.

OVERVIEW OF EXPERIMENTS

- ## *Experiment* 18-1: DEHYDRATING FRUITS AND VEGETABLES

Time Required

Day 1—40 minutes
Day 2—10 minutes

Objective

Students will dehydrate fruits and vegetables and determine the loss of water that occurs by calculating the loss of mass.

Equipment

- 6 triple beam balances/3 electronic balances
- 12 paring knives
- 12 1000-mL beakers
- 12 1000-mL plastic beakers
- dehydrator(s)
- 6–12 trays

Supplies

- 12 0.5-L freezer bags that seal
- sodium bisulfite—1 gram in 1000 mL H_2O
- fruits and vegetables of choice (see below)
- masking tape
- marking pen

Helpful Hints

- Mushrooms and apples tend to lose the most water during drying. Other fruits and vegetables suitable for use are peaches, beans, potatoes, and bananas.
- Remind students of the role of enzymes in browning. Potatoes and bananas will turn very dark during drying unless they undergo some pretreatment. The slice of food soaked in sodium bisulfite gives students a sample to compare with the remaining untreated food. Enzymatic browning is the reason most commercially dehydrated food is subjected to some type of sulfuring process.
- For best accuracy, be sure students slice their samples and *then* determine the mass.
- Remind students that they must not eat any of the massed food either before or after dehydration and rehydration. The temptation to sample is apparently great in this experiment. However, eating the massed food results in inaccurate measurements of the change in mass.
- Set the dehydrator at 57°–63°C.

Laboratory Simplification

Do fewer samples.

Laboratory Enrichment

Students could repeat the experiment with one food sample. At the same time, they could dry the food by oven and room drying. Drying times and the quality of the dried products could be compared.

Expected Data

Results will vary depending on the identity of the samples as well as the length of drying time and the dehydrator.

Food	Mass of Original Sample	Mass of Dried Sample	Mass Lost by Original Sample	Percent of Original Mass Lost as Water	Appearance of Pretreated Slice
Apple	94.6 g	17.03 g	77.57 g	82 percent	light-colored

• Experiment 18-2: RECONSTITUTING FRUITS AND VEGETABLES

Time Required

45 minutes

Objective

Students will discover whether reconstituting dried food samples replaces the water originally lost during dehydration.

Equipment

- 6 triple beam balances/3 electronic balances
- 12 1000-mL beakers
- 12 1000-mL plastic beakers

Supplies

- dried foods from **Experiment 18-1: Dehydrating Fruits and Vegetables**.
- paper towels

Helpful Hints

- The day prior to this experiment, suggest to students that they place their samples in water as soon as they enter the classroom. This will allow the food samples the maximum amount of soaking time before students remove them from the water and mass them.
- Once students have placed the samples in water, they can participate in other activities since there is nothing more to do for the experiment until the last few minutes of the class period.

Laboratory Simplification

Do fewer samples.

Laboratory Enrichment

Rehydrate the foods from the enrichment activity for **Experiment 18-1**. Use various temperatures, such as 1°C, 30°C, and 80°C.

Expected Data

Food	Mass of Dried Sample	Mass of Reconstituted Sample	Mass Gained by Reconstituted Sample	Percent of Reconstituted Mass Gained as Water
Apple	17.03 g	45.47 g	28.44 g	62.5 percent

● *Experiment 18-A:* MAKING RAISINS

Note: The procedure for this experiment is printed only in the *Teacher's Resource Guide.*

Time Required

30 minutes

Objective

Students will use the drying techniques from **Experiment 18-1: Dehydrating Fruits and Vegetables** to make raisins.

Equipment

- 6 triple beam balances/3 electronic balances
- 12 1000-mL plastic beakers
- 12 saucepans
- 12 small strainers
- 12 baking pans

Supplies

- seedless grapes
- paper towels

Helpful Hints

- This experiment can be done by students at home. They can perform it as a simple qualitative exercise by omitting all massing and simply comparing the final product to commercial raisins. Alternately, the grapes can be massed at school, taken home and dried, and brought back to school for massing.
- Depending on climate, you may wish to have students try sun drying grapes to produce raisins. This is also an experiment students could consider in Chapter 22 when they are designing their own experiments.

Expected Data

Data will vary depending on exact drying time, temperature of the oven, and the variety of grape. The more slowly the grapes dry, the less water they will lose.

ANSWER KEY
Student Text

● ANSWERS TO QUESTIONS IN TEXT:

p. 291
The reasons to dehydrate food include that it weighs less, is more compact and lasts for a fairly long time.

p. 293
You should soak vegetables for 5 to 10 minutes when rehydrating.

p. 296
Air must come from an outside source when dehydrating foods in order to remove the moisture.

p. 297
The water content of a mushroom is the same percentage as a strawberry.

p. 299
Dried foods are called nutritional powerhouses because of the high nutritional value per gram. The vitamin loss from blanching is much higher than sulfuring.

● CHECK YOUR FACTS

1. Preserves the food; decreases the weight and bulk of the food to make it easier to transport; and reduces preparation time, which makes dried food more convenient to use.
2. Adding water to dehydrated food.
3. Reduces fat-soluble vitamin loss, flavor loss, enzymatic browning, and deterioration during storage.
4. It extends drying time 15–20 percent because of the water absorbed during soaking.
5. Food maintains its original shape, color, and pliability; does not affect vitamin A and C content; prevents browning; shortens drying time; repels insects; and inhibits the growth of mold.
6. It sets the food's color, denatures enzymes, checks the ripening process, and prevents undesirable flavor changes.
7. Steaming adds less water and causes smaller quantities of water-soluble vitamins and minerals to be lost. It also shortens drying and rehydration time.
8. Adds sugar to already sweet fruit, affects texture and flavor, and reduces vitamin C content of food.

9. It is relatively inexpensive, large quantities can be dried at the same time, and the sun's rays have a sterilizing effect which inhibits the growth of microorganisms.

10. Food does not mold, takes less space than frozen food, has good flavor and color, and reconstitutes in less time than dried food.

11. It provides vitamins and minerals in a very concentrated form.

12. In a sealed glass jar, plastic bag, or metal can at room temperatures.

● CRITICAL THINKING AND PROBLEM SOLVING

1. The pyramids were sealed after the burial ceremonies so air and moisture did not enter the tombs.

2. It is light in weight yet has high nutritional value per gram.

3. They would be hard—the beans need soaking to reconstitute.

4. Advantage is a shorter drying time; disadvantages are more loss of vitamin and minerals and more surface area exposed for enzymatic browning.

5. Vegetables—to deactivate enzymes which would spoil the vegetables; fruits—to stop enzymatic browning.

6. It destroys the natural flavor and texture of the fruit as well as much of the vitamin C and A in the fruit.

7. Their high sugar content and acidity counteracts the enzyme action that would otherwise cause them to spoil.

8. Enzymatic browning in the dried fruit.

9. Drying removes enough moisture from food that bacteria cannot grow in it.

10. They provide a constant temperature, good air circulation, and a sanitary environment.

Student Activity Workbook

● H-18-1: STUDY GUIDE

1. dehydration
2. France
3. reconstitution
4. overnight
5. accelerate (speed)
6. more
7. enzymes
8. oxygen
9. sulfur dioxide gas
10. extends or lengthens
11. sulfuring
12. lungs

13. outside
14. blanching
15. shortens
16. harshest
17. water
18. Steam blanching
19. smaller
20. syrup blanching
21. caseharden
22. rapid
23. Sun drying
24. ultraviolet
25. 29°C
26. dehydrator
27. room drying
28. air circulation
29. Dehydrofreezing
30. high
31. leatherlike
32. 15–20 percent
33. uncovered

● H-18-2: CODED MESSAGES

1. casehardened
2. circulation
3. Syrup blanching
4. dehydrofreezing
5. steam blanched
6. Sulfiting
7. sulfuring
8. reconstituted
9. dehydrator
10. sun drying
11. Dried food has a high nutritional value per gram.

● H-18-3: CROSSWORD PUZZLE

Across
1. caseharden
3. syrup blanching
5. dehydrator
7. room drying
8. rehydration
10. shelf life
11. sulfuring
12. sun drying

Down
2. dehydrofreezing
3. sulfiting
4. reconstitution
6. steam blanching
9. dehydration

● H-18-4: NUTRITION AND YOU

1. nutritional powerhouse
2. Vitamin C, Vitamin A
3. blanching
4. sulfuring
5. more
6. Fewer, lower
7. lower
8. higher
9. 90
10. 7, 29

● Experiment 18-1: DEHYDRATING FRUITS AND VEGETABLES

1. It prevented or slowed enzymatic browning.
2. Answers will vary depending on the foods used.
3. Answers will vary.

4. Answers will vary—mushrooms and apples tend to have the highest moisture content of the fruits and vegetables commonly used.
5. The food with the highest moisture content was the one that underwent the largest percent change in mass.
6. No—bound water cannot be removed by dehydration. It is possible, although not likely, that all the free water was driven off.

● Experiment 18-2: RECONSTITUTING FRUITS AND VEGETABLES

1. Answers will vary depending on the foods used.
2. Answers will vary.

3. No—most samples do not fully restore to their original mass.
4. No—most foods don't completely rehydrate no matter how long they are soaked.

● T-20: DEHYDRATION/REHYDRATION

Answers will vary.

Teacher's Resource Guide

● Experiment 18-A: MAKING RAISINS

1. Answers will vary.

SAFETY: Place your initials under each appropriate symbol to show the safety precautions you need to remember when performing this experiment.

Raisins have been a popular dried food for many years. While most commercially prepared raisins are sun dried, it is possible to produce raisins by drying grapes in a conventional oven. In this experiment, you will prepare raisins and determine the percent of water lost by the grapes in the drying process.

PROCEDURE

1. Wash and dry enough seedless grapes to cover the bottom of a baking pan or dehydrator tray.
2. Fill a small saucepan with tap water and heat to boiling.
3. Mass an empty 100–mL plastic beaker and record its mass. Put the grapes in the beaker and mass the beaker and the grapes. Subtract the mass of the empty beaker from the mass of the beaker and grapes to find the mass of the grapes. Record this value in your data table.
4. Preheat the oven or dehydrator to 63°C (145°F).
5. Using a small strainer, dip the grapes into the saucepan of boiling water. This will split their skins and make them easier to dry.
6. Spread the grapes in a single layer in the baking pan or dehydrator tray and put them in the oven or dehydrator.

7. Turn the grapes at least once while they are being dried.
8. Dry the grapes until they are soft and leathery. This will probably require between 2–4 hours.
9. Remove the grapes from the oven or dehydrator.
10. After the grapes are cooled, determine their mass following the procedure in step 3.
11. Calculate the percent of the original sample that was water. This is the percent of the original mass lost during drying. It can be determined by using the following equation.

$$\text{Percent of original mass lost as water} = \frac{\text{fresh mass} - \text{dried mass}}{\text{fresh mass}} \times 100$$

Record your calculations in your data table.

QUESTIONS

1. How do your raisins compare to your favorite commercial brand of raisins?

SAMPLE DATA TABLE

Mass of Original Sample	Mass of Dried Sample	Mass Lost by Original Sample	Percent of Original Mass Lost as Water

Chapter 18: Dehydration

DEHYDRATION/REHYDRATION

TEXT PAGES 290~303

DIRECTIONS: Use this chart as you do Experiments 18-1 and 18-2 to compare the percentage of water lost and gained when dehydrating and reconstituting fruits and vegetables.

Fruit or Vegetable	Percent of Original Mass Lost as Water	Percent of Reconstituted Mass Gained as Water
Apple—New Zealand		
Apple—Delicious		
Apple—Granny Smith		
Bananas		
Beans		
Cauliflower		
Carrots		
Mushrooms		
Peaches		
Pears		
Peppers		
Potatoes		
Squash		
Zucchini		

CHAPTER

19

Canning

TEXT PAGES 304–318

SUGGESTED TIME SCHEDULE

180-day course—6 days.
90-day course—3 days.

STUDENT OBJECTIVES

- Identify equipment used in home and commercial canning.
- Describe hot–pack and cold–pack methods of preparing food for canning.
- Explain the two methods of processing home-canned food.
- Compare heat transfer by conduction and by convection in canning.
- Discuss the similarities and differences in regular retort canning and aseptic canning.
- Review the properties of C. *botulinum* that make botulism poisoning a problem in improperly canned food.

CHAPTER SUMMARY

- The tempered glass jars usually used in home canning are sealed with a lid held in place by a ring band.
- Canning kettles are used for water bath processing of high–acid food, while pressure canners are needed for pressure processing of low–acid food.
- Food to be canned is packed into containers by either the hot–pack or cold–pack method.
- Processing canned food kills microorganisms and seals the food in an airtight environment.
- Commercial canning is called retort canning because it takes place in huge pressure canners called retorts.
- In retort canning, heat can be transferred by conduction and convection.

- Aseptic canning is fast, economical, and produces canned food with a minimal loss of flavor or nutritional value.
- C. *botulinum* grows anaerobically and produces spores that are resistant to heat and chemicals, making improperly home–canned low–acid food an ideal place for the bacteria to grow and produce toxin.

BACKGROUND INFORMATION

Chapter 19 discusses the topic of canning, a method of food preservation developed in the 1800s. Students will study the procedures and equipment for home and commercial canning. In addition, the properties of C. *botulinum*, which grows in improperly canned food, are discussed in some detail.

This chapter provides an excellent opportunity to reemphasize many of the factors—such as pH, effect of enzymes, and sanitation techniques—that have been previously presented as important in food preservation.

Information from Chapter 4 on methods of heat transfer and the effects of temperature and surface area on cooking time can be reviewed. These factors are critical in determining the processing time for canned food.

Teacher's Resource Guide REPRODUCIBLE MATERIALS

T-21:   Heat Transfer in Canned Foods

ACTIVITIES

1. Survey students to find out how many have done or helped in home canning. What foods have they canned? What do they see as the advantages or disadvantages of home canning?

2. Make applesauce using different kinds of apples. Have students check the pH of the applesauce samples. Discuss whether botulism is a consideration when selecting a processing method for canning applesauce.

3. Divide the applesauce samples and refrigerate one portion of the applesauce. Use the other portion to demonstrate the techniques used in canning applesauce. After the applesauce has been canned, open a can and have students taste test the refrigerated fresh applesauce and the canned applesauce. How did canning affect the color, flavor, texture, and mouthfeel of the applesauce? Do students like the fresh or canned applesauce better? Why?

4. Demonstrate the use of the pressure canner. Stress the correct procedures and the importance of safety in using the pressure canner. Explain why the temperature of the boiling water inside the pressure canner is higher than the temperature of the boiling water in a canning kettle.

5. The FDA *Consumer* carries updates and investigators' reports about current concerns in canning and other methods of preservation.

6. "United States Standards of Processed Fruits and Vegetables and Certain Other Products" published by the U.S. Department of Agriculture is an excellent resource for this chapter.

7. In preparation for **Experiment 19-2: Evaluating Canned Peas**, demonstrate the techniques used in the experiment. Students will need to use care and a light touch to avoid damaging the peas.

8. Use **T-21: Heat Transfer in Canned Foods**. It is printed in the *Guide* and in the *Student Activity Workbook*.

OVERVIEW OF EXPERIMENTS

● *Experiment 19-1:* ENVIRONMENT AND FOOD PRESERVATION

Time Required

Day 1—25 minutes

Day 6—10 minutes

Objective

Students will observe factors that promote or retard the growth of bacteria in food.

Equipment

- 12 250-mL beakers
- 12 tongs
- 72 50-mL beakers or small jars
- 12 saucepans

Supplies

- 2500 mL (2.5 L) chicken broth
- sucrose
- sodium chloride
- lemon juice
- masking tape
- marking pen

Helpful Hints

- Instead of making one batch of chicken broth, each laboratory group can dissolve 1 bullion cube in 200 mL water in a 250-mL beaker.
- Stress the importance of handling the samples with care. Since the experiment is designed to test for airborne bacteria, bacteria from other sources will provide incorrect data.
- Store all the samples in the same environment. Do not cover the samples. It is preferable to store them in a location where they are open to the air, but they could be stored in a cupboard, if necessary.

Laboratory Simplification

Do beakers C and F.

Laboratory Enrichment

Have students repeat the experiment, but have them refrigerate the samples instead of storing them at room temperature. What do students conclude about the effect of refrigeration on mold growth?

Expected Data

Data will vary with the cleanliness of the equipment, the care with which students handled the samples, and the variable added. In general, the samples containing lemon juice and salt will produce less mold and minimal changes in broth color, odor, and appearance. The control sample and those to which sugar or water were added generally display varying amounts of mold by the end of the experiment.

● Experiment 19-2: EVALUATING CANNED PEAS

Time Required

35 minutes

Objective

Students will evaluate canned peas by looking for evidence that the sugar found in young peas has turned to the starch found in older peas.

Equipment

- 18 250-mL beakers
- 12 100-mL graduated cylinders
- 6 can openers

Supplies

- 1 can each of 6 different brands of canned peas
- paper towels
- sodium chloride
- 1000 mL brine solution (see below)
- masking tape
- marking pen

Helpful Hints

- Prepare a 15 percent salt solution by dissolving 150 g sodium chloride in 850 mL water.
- Two pairs of partners can share a can of peas. Have students open the can, drain the liquid in the can into a 250 mL beaker, and label the beaker with the brand name of the peas. Ask students to place the beakers with the liquid in a location where all students can see the variation in color and clarity of the liquids.
- Remind students to handle the peas carefully to avoid damage that would give incorrect data.
- After students have completed the experiment and reported their data on the chalkboard, provide the unit cost of each brand of peas. Students can compare the unit cost with the quality of each brand of peas. The best quality have clear liquid in the can, very few peas with broken skins, and peas that float. These properties indicate sweet young peas with a high sugar/low starch content.

Laboratory Simplification

Compare three brands only.

Laboratory Enrichment

Use kidney or lima beans instead of peas.

Expected Data

Results will vary from brand to brand.

ANSWER KEY
Student Text

● ANSWERS TO QUESTIONS IN TEXT:

p. 305

The high temperatures used in canning kill the bacteria that cause food spoilage.

p. 308

1. Canned foods do not usually contain Vitamin C and thiamin.
2. Since riboflavin can be destroyed by light, canned foods packed in glass should be stored in the dark.

p. 309   85 minutes

p. 312

Pouch canning allows for shorter processing time which produces a higher quality product while using less energy. In addition, pouches weigh less and take up less space than more rigid containers.

● CHECK YOUR FACTS

1. Microorganisms cannot enter the sealed can and contaminate the food.
2. Containers, lids, ring bands, and a canner.
3. Wide mouth jars—they are easy to fill.
4. So the boiling water can circulate under and around the containers.
5. The cold food is placed in containers and covered with a hot liquid in the cold-pack method. In the hot-pack method, the food and liquid are both heated before being placed in the containers.
6. So you will know how to process a specific food and how long to process it.
7. High-acid foods, such as fruits, tomatoes, and pickles.
8. Higher temperatures are needed to kill the harmful microorganisms.
9. It is done in huge pressure canners called retorts.

10. It has been heated in a large pressurized cooker so that all pathogenic or toxin-forming organisms have been destroyed.
11. Advantages—speed and minimal loss of flavor or nutrients; disadvantages—total control of sanitary conditions must be maintained.
12. Pressure processing to a temperature of 140°C.

● CRITICAL THINKING AND PROBLEM SOLVING

1. The cost of canning equipment and supplies as compared to the cost of prepared applesauce; whether you have the time to can the applesauce—the cost of your time.
2. Answers may vary. Generally, applesauce is hot-packed and processed in a water bath for about 20 minutes.
3. The jar would not seal.
4. The 454 g can—larger containers take longer to process.
5. The sweet potatoes will take longer than the peas because it will take more time for heat to penetrate to the center of the larger pieces of potato. There is apt to be more heat transfer due to convection in the peas than in the sweet potatoes.
6. C. *botulinum* grows anaerobically and canned food provides perfect conditions for anaerobic growth.
7. Answers will vary.

Student Activity Workbook

● H-19-1: STUDY GUIDE

1. Nicolas Appert; Napoleon, Emperor of France.
2. Low-acid foods, such as green beans or corn—they are not acidic enough to prevent the growth of microorganisms.
3. Creating a sealed airtight environment for the food.
4. After processing while the food is cooling.
5. Food with a low density that may fall apart when cooked.
6. Hot-pack.
7. Less—the heat of processing destroys some vitamins; water-soluble vitamins and minerals dissolve in the liquid used in canning.
8. Water-bath processing and pressure processing. The temperatures are higher in pressure processing.

9. Commercial canning using pressure canners called retorts.
10. Pressure processing.
11. Up to two years.
12. Conduction—there is no liquid or air to transfer heat by convection.
13. To shorten processing time by increasing the movement of the food.
14. The location in a container that takes the longest to heat to a desired temperature.
15. The center of the can; slightly below the center of the can.
16. Canning in a soft, pliable container.
17. Canning in which the food and the container are both sterilized before the food is put into the container.
18. Aseptically—the speed of processing reduces the exposure of the food to heat, so fewer nutrients are lost.
19. Boiled to at least 80°C for 10 minutes.
20. In soil.

● H-19-2: CANNING CALLS

1. raw-pack
2. cold point
3. pouch canning
4. water-bath processing
5. hot-pack
6. retorts
7. aseptic canning
8. pressure processing
9. agitation retort
10. thiamin

● H-19-3: NUTRITION AND YOU

1. The nutritional value of canned food is generally less than that of fresh food because the high temperatures used in canning will cause heat-sensitive nutrients to break down.
2. Carbohydrates and fats are not generally affected by the heat used in canning.
3. Canned foods do not usually contain Vitamin C and thiamin.
4. Because tomatoes are a high-acid food, they can be processed at lower temperatures, and therefore retain more vitamin C than other canned foods.
5. Water soluble nutrients are lost when they dissolve in the liquid in canned foods.
6. If the canning liquid is used when a canned food is prepared or served, the vitamins and minerals will not go to waste.

7. Fruit packed in fruit juice is more nutritious than fruit packed in heavy sugar syrup because it does not contain the empty kilocalories found in heavy syrup.
8. Tuna packed in water has fewer kilocalories than tuna packed in oil.
9. High storage temperatures and light can cause nutritional value to be lost from canned food.
10. Food canned in glass jars should be stored in the dark.

● T-21: HEAT TRANSFER IN CANNED FOODS

1. conduction
2. convection

● *Experiment* 19-1: ENVIRONMENT AND FOOD PRESERVATION

1. Information in data table.
2. Information in data table.

3. Answers will vary depending on how sanitary the laboratory area and equipment were. There will be less mold growth in the samples containing lemon juice and salt. The lemon juice lowers the pH. Both the lowered pH and the salt inhibit the growth of microorganisms.
4. There would have been less mold and bacteria growth in all samples.

● *Experiment* 19-2: EVALUATING CANNED PEAS

1. Information in data table.
2. Information in data table.
3. Yes, more peas sank when there were more broken skins.
4. Yes, more peas from the cloudier brine sank.
5. Answers will vary.
6. Not necessarily. Answers will vary.

Chapter 19: Canning

HEAT TRANSFER IN CANNED FOODS

T E X T   P A G E S   3 0 4 ~ 3 1 8

DIRECTIONS: Identify the types of heating indicated by the arrows in each illustration.

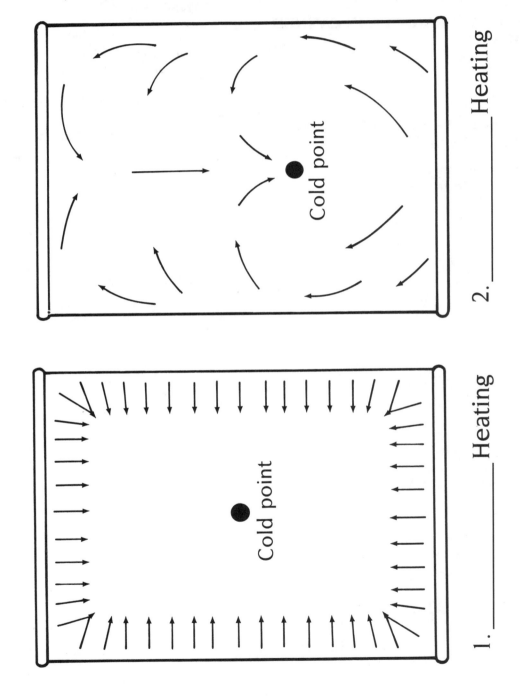

Heating

Cold point

2. _____

Heating

Cold point

1. _____

CHAPTER 20

New Techniques of Food Preservation

TEXT PAGES 319—333

SUGGESTED TIME SCHEDULE

180-day course—6 days.
90-day course—2 days.

STUDENT OBJECTIVES

- Examine the factors needed for successful freezing of food.
- Explain the role of sublimation in freeze drying.
- Identify examples of food that can successfully be freeze-dried and tell how they should be stored.
- Describe the process of food irradiation and its effect on food being irradiated.
- Define the units used to measure the amount of radiation used during irradiation.
- Discuss the effect the Delaney Anti-Cancer Clause has had on the irradiated food industry.
- List properties of containers needed for commercial food packaging.
- Identify factors related to the successful use of controlled-atmosphere packaging.

CHAPTER SUMMARY

- The packaging selected for home and commercial freezing affects the quality of the frozen food.
- Freeze drying takes place in a special chamber in which the water in a frozen food is removed by sublimation.
- Freeze-dried food is lightweight, has a long shelf life, and is reconstituted before being eaten.
- Irradiation is a cold preservation method that involves passing gamma and beta rays through a food sample.
- The radiation used in irradiation is measured in rads, grays, and krads.

- Irradiation is regulated by the FDA, which approves food for irradiation only when it is shown that the irradiated food does not cause cancer.
- Containers for packaging food commercially should be nontoxic, sanitary, durable, easy to use, attractive, and economical.
- Controlled-atmosphere packaging involves altering the gaseous environment around a food.

BACKGROUND INFORMATION

Chapter 20 introduces students to the newer techniques of food preservation. Freezing, freeze drying, and irradiation are explained. In addition, controlled-atmosphere packaging (CAP) is discussed.

This chapter deals with an area that is changing almost daily. Checking in the library for recently published articles related to food preservation will help you keep abreast of the newest information in this field, especially about irradiation.

A common example of the sublimation that takes place in freeze drying is when clothes are hung on the line in subfreezing weather. The clothes dry, even though the water on them exists as ice the entire time they are on the line. Another example of sublimation is when moth balls disappear. Eskimos have been freeze drying for years. They place small animals they have killed on a line and allow the freezing wind to remove the water present in the animals at the time of death.

Sublimation has many uses in addition to freeze drying food. Freeze drying is used in storing blood. As early as World War II, blood plasma was freeze dried so it could be sent to field hospitals. There it was rehydrated with sterile water and used. Freeze drying is also used in taxidermy, where many small animals are now preserved by freeze drying them.

- "What's C.A.P.?" *Food Engineering*, February 1985, page 54.
- Beatrice Hunter, "Packaging Atmosphere," *Consumers' Research*, November 1986, page 8.

ACTIVITIES

1. Discuss with students the frozen foods they use at home. How many students have participated in freezing food at home? What foods are commonly frozen at home? What commercially frozen foods are commonly used in students' homes? What are the advantages and disadvantages of freezing as a method of preservation?

2. Explain sublimation and how it is used in the process of freeze-drying foods.

3. Have samples of freeze-dried foods available for students to examine. These are generally available at backpacking stores. Mass the foods, and rehydrate them. Mass the foods again, and calculate the mass added to these foods when they are rehydrated. Have students evaluate the taste of the reconstituted freeze-dried foods compared to canned or frozen samples of the same foods. Compare the cost of the freeze-dried samples with the canned or frozen samples.

4. Discuss irradiation and how food can be preserved by this process. Why is it controversial? What are the pros and cons of using irradiation? Use **T-22: Irradiation** to help explain this method of food preservation. It is printed in the *Guide* and in the *Student Activity Workbook*.

5. Discuss how packaging affects food preservation. What are the most common types of packages used on snack foods students eat? Why are these packaging methods chosen? Explain controlled-atmosphere packaging (CAP). Why is it an improvement over other packaging methods? How does it prevent rancidity? What other advantages does CAP have?

6. Have students read and discuss one or more of the following articles:
   - "Freeze-drying Technique Makes for Movable Feasts," *Smithsonian*, July 1983, page 91.
   - "Food Fight over Gamma Rays," *Time*, September 22, 1986, page 65.
   - "Irradiation: A Ray of Hope for Our Food?" *Current Health*, October 1985, page 20.

OVERVIEW OF EXPERIMENTS

• *Experiment* 20-1: EFFECT OF LIGHT ON FLAVOR

Time Required

Day 1—10 minutes
Daily checks—5 minutes

Objective

Students will evaluate potato chips stored in different environments for a two-week period to determine the effect of light on flavor.

Equipment

- 24 400-mL beakers

Supplies

- 1 package regular potato chips
- 1 package flavored potato chips
- 1 roll aluminum foil
- 1 roll plastic wrap
- masking tape
- marking pen

Helpful Hints

- Have half the class use flavored chips and half regular chips. If possible, have one-third of the class store their samples in a drawer or cupboard; one-third store them in daylight, preferably where they will be exposed to the hot afternoon sun; and one-third on a countertop where they will be exposed to artificial lighting only. Divide the groups so that two with flavored and two with unflavored samples store the chips in each location. This will make it possible to see how rapidly different amounts and kinds of light cause fats to turn rancid, as well as how effective the flavoring is at masking different degrees of rancid flavor.
- In the discussion following the completion of the experiment, ask whether the rancid flavor was masked in the flavored chips and whether sunlight increased rancidity more than artificial lighting.

Laboratory Simplification

None.

Laboratory Enrichment

Perform lab using corn tortilla chips.

Expected Data

Results will vary depending on the chips and storage conditions.

● Experiment 20-2: COMPARISON OF ORANGE JUICES

Time Required

30 minutes

Objective

Students will compare samples of fresh, frozen, freeze-dried, aseptically-processed, and pouch-canned orange juice for color, mouthfeel, taste, and cost.

Equipment

● 5 1-L pitchers

Supplies

● 120 28-mL paper cups
● 1 L fresh squeezed orange juice

● 1 L reconstituted frozen orange juice
● 1 L reconstituted freeze-dried orange juice
● 1 L pouch-canned orange juice
● 1 L aseptically-canned orange juice
● masking tape
● marking pen

Helpful Hints

● Mix the juices before class and place them in pitchers numbered with three-digit numbers such as those in the data table below.
● Each student should take five 28-mL cups for tasting the samples of orange juice. Have students label each cup with the number of the juice they put into it. Students should rinse their mouths with water between tasting each sample.
● After students have tasted all samples, post the processing method and the unit cost of each numbered sample on the chalkboard.
● Discuss why students prefer their favorite juices. For example, some students may not like pulp in their juice, so they may not like the fresh orange juice.

Laboratory Simplification

Use three variations only.

Laboratory Enrichment

Repeat experiment with another type of fruit juice.

Expected Data

Sample	Color	Mouthfeel	Taste	Unit Cost	Preservation Method
134	dark orange	pulpy	excellent		fresh
461	orange	some pulp, tart	very good		frozen
223	orange	grainy	sweet, good		freeze drying
927	yellow	watery smooth	sour, strong		aseptically canned
704	light yellow	watery	bland, sour		pouch canned

ANSWER KEY

Student Text

● ANSWERS TO QUESTIONS IN TEXT:

p. 324

The shortest radio waves are called microwaves.

p. 327

Spices have been irradiated since 1986.

p. 328

CAP stands for meat that has been packaged in a controlled-atmosphere package such as chicken in an atmosphere which is 100% carbon dioxide.

p. 329

1. Straws are used a lot in space to keep liquids from floating around in the air.
2. Typical desserts found in a space lab are chocolate pudding, applesauce, cookies and granola bars.

● CHECK YOUR FACTS

1. Vegetables should be blanched. The food should be put in a suitable container, tightly sealed, and labeled.
2. The ice in the food changes to a gas and escapes, leaving a rigid frozen product that looks like a sponge because the places in the food that held water are empty.
3. Expense.
4. Flavors, cultured microorganisms, enzymes, and specialty chemicals.
5. They destroy living organisms in the food that would cause it to spoil.
6. A substance shown to cause cancer in humans or animals may not be added to a food in any amount.
7. To inhibit sprouting.
8. To control *Salmonella* contamination.
9. A faulty package can allow contamination by microorganisms and/or rehydration of dried food.
10. The meat industry.

● CRITICAL THINKING AND PROBLEM SOLVING

1. They are similar because they both involve dehydration and freezing. However, in freeze drying,

food is frozen and then dried. In dehydrofreezing, the food is dehydrated and then frozen.
2. To get the ice in food to sublime as quickly as possible.
3. The irradiated food is not radioactive.
4. Slowed its use because each specific food product must be tested individually.
5. No—irradiation inhibits sprouting, so the eyes would be unlikely to grow before they rotted.
6. Answers will vary.
7. It is light and therefore adds as little weight as possible on liftoff.
8. Answers will vary.

Student Activity Workbook

● H-20-1: STUDY GUIDE

1.	convenient	19.	gamma and beta
2.	-18	20.	cold
3.	burn	21.	rad
4.	air	22.	1000 krads
5.	indirect-contact	23.	FDA
6.	immersion	24.	food additive
7.	10	25.	Delaney Anti-Cancer Clause
8.	solvent		
9.	lyophilization	26.	one-by-one
10.	sublimation	27.	contamination
11.	lowered	28.	opaque
12.	flash freezing	29.	heat-resistant
13.	99	30.	controlled-atmosphere packaging
14.	lightweight		
15.	higher		
16.	radiation	31.	gaseous environment
17.	infrared		
18.	Irradiated	32	inert (nonreactive)
		33.	dehydrated

● H-20-2: SECRET WORD

1.	space	7.	gray
2.	nutritious	8.	nitrogen
3.	C. *botulinum*	9.	spices
4.	lyophilization	10.	potato
5.	radiation	11.	hundred
6.	gamma		

The secret word is sublimation.

● H-20-3: NUTRITION AND YOU

1. 1960s
2. gravity
3. limited
4. Crumbs
5. 6 months, 37.7°C
6. compact, lightweight
7. dehydrated
8. cookies, peanut butter, granola bars, candy
9. pouched, canned
10. earth

● T-22: IRRADIATION

1. energy
2. grays
3. electromagnetic
4. preservation
5. irradiated
6. metal-plate
7. cold food
8. food additive
9. Food and Drug Administration
10. nutrients
11. immediately
12. odor

● Experiment 20-1: EFFECT OF LIGHT ON FLAVOR

1. Information in data table.
2. It blocked out light.
3. The fat became rancid.
4. They are packaged in containers that exclude at least some light so the fat will not become rancid during storage.

● Experiment 20-2: COMPARISON OF ORANGE JUICES

1. Sample 134 looks the most like fresh orange juice.
2. Sample 134 felt the most like fresh orange juice—it was pulpy.
3. Sample 134 had the best flavor.
4. Answers will vary.
5. Answers will vary.
6. The freeze-dried orange juice. It would be lightweight, easy to carry, and easy to reconstitute.

Chapter 20: New Techniques of Food Preservation

IRRADIATION

TEXT PAGES 319-333

DIRECTIONS: Fill in the blanks below.

Radiation is:

1. The transfer of _____ through space in waves.

2. Measured in rads, _____ and krads.

3. Shown on the _____ spectrum.

4. Used in several ways in food processing and _____.

5. Not given off by food that has been _____.

Irradiation:

6. Takes place in a _____-_____ irradiation room.

7. Is called a _____ _____ preservation method.

8. Is classified as a _____ _____.

9. Is regulated by the _____ _____ _____

   _____.

10. Uses low temperatures so _____ are not destroyed.

11. Leaves no residue so food can be eaten _____.

12. Has little effect on the flavor, color, and _____ of food.

CHAPTER

21

Additives

TEXT PAGES 334–349

SUGGESTED TIME SCHEDULE

180-day course—8 days.
90-day course—6 days.

STUDENT OBJECTIVES

- Identify agencies involved in regulating food additives.
- Discuss the various purposes food additives serve.
- Describe properties of a desirable food preservative.
- Explain why additives used as antioxidants are added to food.
- Differentiate between natural and artificial additives.
- Identify kinds of sweeteners used in food processing.
- Name several nutrients that are used as food additives.
- Discuss the advantages and disadvantages of using food additives.

CHAPTER SUMMARY

- A food additive is a substance added intentionally to food to improve appearance, flavor, texture, nutritional value, or storage properties.
- The use of food additives is regulated by the FDA in the United States and by the FAO and WHO on the international level.
- Food additives used as preservatives help extend the shelf life of food products and prevent spoilage when food is transported long distances.
- Antioxidants prevent the breakdown of fat and vitamins that occurs when a food combines with oxygen.
- Additives can be used to improve the color and flavor of food.

- Nutritional value can be added to food through fortification, restoration, enrichment, or nutrification.
- Although additives are included in food for constructive purposes, some people feel that additives are nutritionally worthless and harmful to health.

BACKGROUND INFORMATION

Food additives are one of the most controversial topics associated with food science. Chapter 21 presents students with information on the reasons additives are used, as well as facts about artificial and natural additives.

Additives are not always synthetic compounds prepared in research laboratories. The substances most commonly added during food processing are sodium chloride and sucrose—salt and sugar.

Although salt and sugar are commonly added to foods, they are not always used simply to enhance flavor. Salt, for example, is a necessary ingredient in hot dogs. It is used to bind the particles of meat together in a gel texture. Salt also retards the rate of spoilage. Salt is used in other areas of food processing to control microbial growth. It controls the growth of microorganisms by lowering the water activity level in a food.

Teacher's Resource Guide
REPRODUCIBLE MATERIALS

T-23:   Using Additives

ACTIVITIES

1. Most supermarket chains have pamphlets on additives—what they are and why they are used. Often classroom sets are available for the asking.

2. Discuss with students what additives are, how they are used in food processing, the difference between natural and artificial additives, and the functions of additives. Use **T-23: Using Additives** to highlight the various roles additives play in food processing. It is printed in the *Guide*.

3. Show the film: "Salt and Hypertension: How to Save Your Life," PYRA, 1982 (26 minutes).

4. Have students look at food labels to identify the various additives contained in each food and the function of the additives in the foods. Have students use **H-21-3: Analyzing Labels** to record their findings. It is printed in the *Guide*.

5. Have students read and discuss one or more of the following articles:
   - "The Sweet Stuff," *Current Health*, January 1985, page 16.
   - "The Food Industry and the Salt Shaker," *Science of Food and Agriculture Journal*, January 1984, page 21.
   - "Food Labels—Test Your Food Label Knowledge," FDA *Consumer*, March 1988, page 16.
   - "Much Ado About Food," *Current Health*, December 1986, page 22.

EXTENSION ACTIVITIES

1. Select a white cake recipe and vary the ingredient that adds sweetness. Sugar, an aspartame product, and a saccharin product are possible variables. The appearance, odor, flavor, and mouthfeel of the cakes could be evaluated.

OVERVIEW OF EXPERIMENTS

• *Experiment 21-1:* PUDDING MIXES AND ADDITIVES

Time Required

Day 1—45 minutes
Day 2—25 minutes

Objective

Students will observe the effect of various additives on vanilla pudding.

Equipment

- 12 small saucepans
- 12 measuring cups
- 12 100-mL graduated cylinders
- 12 line-spread sheets
- 12 plastic rings (cylinders) 50.1 mm wide and 25.4 mm high
- 12 glass pie plates
- 2–4 muffin tins

Supplies

- 12 boxed vanilla pudding mixes that require cooking.
- 1 box baker's paper soufflé cups
- sucrose
- lemon juice
- masking tape
- marking pen

Helpful Hints

- Use the same rings that were used in **Experiment 7-2: Thickening Agents**. Remind students how to read the line-spread sheets, which were also used in that experiment. (These can be laminated for repeated use.)
- Label the muffin tins ahead of time with the variation numbers. The number of tins needed will depend on the size of the class and the size of the tins.

Laboratory Simplification

Do variations 1 and 2 only.

Laboratory Enrichment

Perform experiment using butterscotch or chocolate pudding mix.

Expected Data

Variation	Line-spread Average		Appearance Refrigerated Sample	Appearance Frozen Sample
	Hot	Cold		
1	12	8	runny no syneresis	slightly runny much syneresis
2	15	8	stiffer than regular	slightly runny much syneresis
3	5	3	slightly stiff no syneresis	gooey, stiff no syneresis

● Experiment 21-2: TESTING FOR FOOD ADDITIVES

Time Required

45 minutes

Objective

Students will determine whether or not sulfuring has been used in the preservation of various dried fruit samples.

Equipment

- 12 400-mL beakers
- 12 stirring rods
- 12 funnels
- 12 250-mL beakers
- 12 100-mL graduated cylinders
- 12 dropping bottles

Supplies

- 3–4 types of dried fruit
- deionized or distilled water
- 12 10-cm squares of cheesecloth
- 1.5 L of 3% hydrogen peroxide
- 500 mL of 1.0 N $BaCl_2$ solution (divided into 12 dropping bottles)

Helpful Hints

- Fruits used will depend partly on availability. Those likely to have been exposed to sulfuring include apricots, apples, golden raisins, peaches and pears, while prunes, dark raisins and figs probably would not have been.

- 3% hydrogen peroxide can be purchased at most grocery stores or pharmacies. Or, 30% hydrogen peroxide can be purchased from chemical companies and then diluted using 100 mL of the concentrated peroxide in 1000 mL of dilute. However, if 30% hydrogen peroxide is used, wear rubber gloves when handling it, as it will oxidize skin.
- The barium chloride solution can be prepared by dissolving 104 g of the solid in deionized water and diluting to 500 mL. Since only a few drops are used for each test, this amount should last for some time.

Expected Data

Results will vary.

ANSWER KEY

Student Text

● ANSWERS TO QUESTIONS IN TEXT:

p. 335

Saccharin was removed from the GRAS list because extensive testing showed it could produce cancer in laboratory animals.

p. 336

Vanilla ice cream contains actual beans or vanilla bean extract , while vanilla flavored ice cream contains either all artificial vanilla flavoring or a combination of real vanilla and artificial vanilla flavoring.

p. 338

Ascorbic acid is used as an antioxidant, nutrient, and color stabilizer in foods.

1. The first fortified food was iodized salt.
2. Milk is fortified with Vitamin D to help prevent rickets.

● CHECK YOUR FACTS

1. A substance added intentionally to food to improve it.
2. To improve appearance, flavor, texture, or storage properties of food.
3. It prohibits their use if there is evidence they may cause cancer in animals or humans.
4. Special legislation was passed to allow its use.
5. Only 1/100 of the amount of an additive found to be safe in testing with laboratory animals can be added to food.
6. Nontoxic; economical; and don't affect the flavor, color, or texture of the foods to which they are added.
7. To protect consumers from botulism.
8. A substance used to slow down or prohibit oxidation.
9. To inhibit crystallization, to stabilize foam, or to reduce stickiness.
10. Natural additives are normal components of natural food products, while artificial additives are made in a chemical laboratory.
11. Alginate, casein, gums, vitamin E, vitamin C, citric acid, beta carotene.
12. To enhance the appearance of food.
13. There are not enough natural flavorings available.
14. To include additives for their nutritive value.
15. To chemically trap tiny bits of metal that enter the food during the manufacturing process.

● CRITICAL THINKING AND PROBLEM SOLVING

1. 1 mg or less.
2. Vanilla ice cream would contain actual particles of vanilla beans or extract from vanilla beans. Artificially-flavored vanilla ice cream would contain either artificial vanilla flavoring or a mixture of artificial and natural flavorings.
3. To help prevent the formation of large crystals that would give the ice cream a grainy texture.
4. Saccharin should not be used in large amounts because it has been shown to cause cancer in animals, and it is not known in what amounts it may

be dangerous to humans. Aspartame should not be overused because, although it contains naturally-occurring amino acids, they are a combination that would normally be consumed in only very small quantities.
5. Iodine is added to prevent goiter; vitamin D is added to prevent rickets.
6. All involve adding nutrients to food. However, fortification is a general term that means adding nutrients not normally found in the food. Restoration is adding back nutrients that were removed by processing. Enrichment adds more of nutrients found naturally in the food. Nutrification adds a balance of nutrients to a food in which they are not normally found.
7. Good nutrition comes from eating a variety of foods. Eating a nutrified food in place of other foods does not provide the needed variety, so is an unhealthy eating habit.
8. Answers will vary.
9. Answers will vary.

Student Activity Workbook

● H-21-1: STUDY GUIDE

1. The Food and Drug Administration.
2. Spices, natural seasonings, flavorings.
3. To deceive the consumer; decrease the nutritional value of a food; to conceal damage, spoilage, or low quality in a food.
4. The ice cream may contain natural banana flavor plus other natural flavors.
5. So food can be transported long distances; to increase shelf life.
6. Sodium nitrite, sodium bisulfite, sorbic acid, sodium nitrate.
7. Oxygen.
8. Vitamins and lipids break down; changes occur in color and flavor.
9. Salt water, sulfur, vitamin E, ascorbic acid, lecithin.
10. Thickeners.
11. Prevent the fat from separating from the protein.
12. They come from a food or a specific part of a plant.
13. Antioxidants.
14. Citric acid, sodium citrate, lactic acid, sodium bicarbonate, sodium hydroxide.
15. By number.
16. 2000.

17. Sugar and other sweeteners.
18. Aspartic acid and phenylalanine.
19. Contaminants.
20. To remove any pesticides present.

● H-21-2: MAGIC SQUARE

A. 2	**E.** 8	**I.** 13	**M.** 16
B. 7	**F.** 5	**J.** 17	**N.** 10
C. 18	**G.** 11	**K.** 6	**O.** 4
D. 12	**H.** 15	**L.** 3	**P.** 9

The magic number is 39.

● H-21-3: ANALYZING LABELS

Answers will vary.

● H-21-4: NUTRITION AND YOU

1.	i	6.	f
2.	j	7.	a
3.	h	8.	d
4.	g	9.	b
5.	c	10.	e

● Experiment 21-1: PUDDING MIXES AND ADDITIVES

1. The viscosity and color differed. Some samples were opaque, others translucent.
2. Variation 2—it shows less runniness.
3. The pudding became translucent, very stiff, and displayed no runniness.
4. There was no change in color but a less runny product was produced because the sugar bound the water.
5. Varying degrees of syneresis occurred.
6. Some were extremely stiff, others were extremely runny, with a great deal of syneresis.
7. The additives did about the same thing as the starches used in **Experiment 7-2**. By binding the water, they prevented syneresis (to varying degrees).

● Experiment 21-2: TESTING FOR FOOD ADDITIVES

1. Answers will vary depending on fruits used.
2. Exposure to sulfur dioxide prevents enzymatic browning while preserving the original shape and color of the fruit. It also shortens drying time, repels insects, and inhibits mold growth. Finally, sulfuring does not affect the vitamin A and C contained in the fruit.
3. They would eventually turn brown and spoil.
4. Answers will vary. Possibilities include: artificial color, sugar, or vitamin C.
5. Answers will vary.

Using Additives

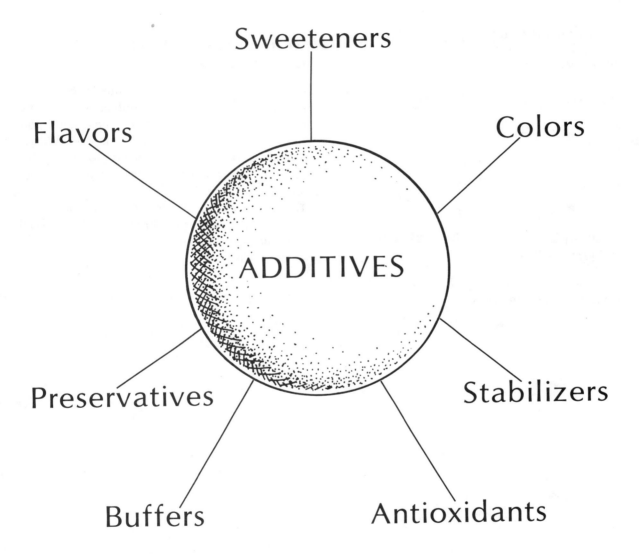

Sweeteners

Colors

Flavors

ADDITIVES

Preservatives

Stabilizers

Buffers

Antioxidants

CHAPTER 22

Developing Experiments in Food Science

TEXT PAGES 352–363

SUGGESTED TIME SCHEDULE

180-day course—9 days.
90-day course—4 days.

STUDENT OBJECTIVES

- Describe ways of choosing a topic for a food science research project.
- Identify resources that can be used to gather information for a research topic.
- Select a hypothesis and title for a food science experiment.
- Propose variables for a food science experiment.
- Develop a procedure for a food science experiment.
- Explain the importance of accurate supply and equipment lists for a food science experiment.

CHAPTER SUMMARY

- A topic chosen for a research project should be of interest so the researcher does not get bored before the project is done.
- The card catalog, a computer search, or the *Reader's Guide to Periodical Literature* can lead to books and magazine articles that contain information on a particular subject.
- The focus of a research project must be narrowed so it can be finished in the time available.
- The hypothesis of an experiment is a proposed solution to a scientific problem.
- The variables in an experiment are the factors being tested.
- Several trials of an experiment are run to be sure results are consistent so valid conclusions can be drawn.
- A data table is used to record experiment results in an organized manner.

BACKGROUND INFORMATION

Chapter 22 provides students with the opportunity to develop experiments in areas of food science that they find interesting. The chapter presents information on how to investigate a topic and develop an experiment. A case example describing the development of **Experiment 22–1: Properties of Popping Corn** is given.

This is the time when students can synthesize the knowledge they have gained throughout the course as they take an in-depth look at a topic of their choosing. If necessary, you can suggest topics of particular merit or interest.

Teacher's Resource Guide REPRODUCIBLE MATERIALS

T-24:   Parts of an Experiment

ACTIVITIES

1. Take students to the library and review the resources available for locating information related to food science topics. Be sure students know how to use the card catalog, the *Reader's Guide to Periodical Literature*, and any computerized data bases the library may have.
2. Discuss what a bibliography is and how it is used in research projects. Show examples of the format the bibliography should take and explain that interviews and other personal contacts should be included with the customary list of books and articles.

3. Discuss the procedures for developing an experiment. Use **T-24: Parts of an Experiment** to help students plan their experiments. It is printed in the *Guide* and in the *Student Activity Workbook*.
4. Before students read the information in the text on the development of **Experiment 22-1: Properties of Popping Corn**, have them read and discuss the following article: Lynn K. Sibley, "Popcorn," *Chem Matters*, October 1984, page 10.
5. Have students research, plan, and conduct a food science experiment. In addition, have them prepare a paper summarizing their library research and experimental findings.
6. Show the film: "How to Make a Junk Food," NOVA, 1987 (60 minutes).

OVERVIEW OF EXPERIMENTS

● *Experiment* 22-1: PROPERTIES OF POPPING CORN

Time Required

Day 1—10 minutes
Day 2—20 minutes

Objective

Students will determine what factors cause popping corn to pop.

Equipment

- 1 (or more) hot air popcorn popper
- 1 dehydrator
- 12 pins with plastic heads
- 12 bowls

Supplies

- 1 unopened bag of popping corn

Helpful Hints

- A hot air popper gives more consistent results than one that uses oil.
- Preheat the popper or the first batch of corn that is popped will yield more unpopped kernels than it should.
- If more than one hot air popper is available, have equal numbers of groups popping each variation at each popper.

- Popcorn that has been kept in a semisealed container for a long period of time (several months) will produce roughly the same percent of unpopped kernels as the corn dried in the dehydrator.
- Heating the popcorn, which dries it out, has more of an effect on popping than puncturing the popcorn has. In addition to the fact that fewer kernels of the dried popcorn pop, some students may notice that the volume of the popped kernels is smaller than that of the fresh undried popcorn. This concept is pursued further in Extension Activity 1.

Laboratory Simplification

None.

Laboratory Enrichment

Have students repeat the experiment but measure the volume of popped corn produced in each variation.

Expected Data

Variation	Number of Unpopped Kernels	Percent Unpopped Kernels
1	85	21
2	152	38
3	102	25

● *Experiment* 22-2: A TASTE OF TASTE TESTING

Time Required

Day 1—25 minutes
Day 2—20 minutes

Objective

Students will develop a taste test experiment and perform their procedure with their classmates.

Supplies

- 1 L each of three brands of cola
- 1 L of a noncola soft drink
- 28-mL paper cups
- materials for blindfolds

Helpful Hints

- Divide the class into groups of four and have each group develop an experimental procedure. The groups can then carry out their procedure with the other groups serving as subjects. By using groups of four, it should be possible to complete the laboratory work in a reasonable amount of time.
- It is a good idea to have some strips of cloth available in case some students want to blindfold their subjects.

ANSWER KEY
Student Text

● ANSWERS TO QUESTIONS IN TEXT:

p. 355

The experiment designed by Lavoisier was to test the theory of breathing and respiration as a measurable chemical process. Magendie concluded dogs needed protein to live.

p. 358

Trial 1, Trial 2, and Trial 3 are different tests during an experiment.

● CHECK YOUR FACTS

1. Review the literature that exists on the topic.
2. The FDA *Consumer, Food Technology, Food Engineering,* the *Journal of Food Science,* and the *Journal of the American Dietetic Association.*
3. Talk to people knowledgeable in your area of interest.
4. The time available for carrying out the experiment, the resources available when you want to do the experiment, and the space and equipment available in your classroom.
5. To state the purpose or the hypothesis you are trying to prove.
6. So you can give others an idea of what you are trying to show in the experiment.

7. So there are not so many possible explanations for what happens that you are unable to decide what caused the final results.
8. So your results can be recorded in an organized manner.
9. They help you be efficient when conducting the experiment.
10. A title, a paragraph explaining the purpose of the experiment, a step-by-step procedure, a data table, and any questions you hope to answer.

● CRITICAL THINKING AND PROBLEM SOLVING

1. There isn't time or resources to do a broad project, so it is necessary to choose a topic with a narrow focus.
2. So the type of bowl doesn't affect the results.
3. To see if results are consistent.
4. A watch with a second hand or a stop watch would be useful to be certain that all samples are whipped for the same length of time; a thermometer to be certain that all samples are the same temperature.
5. Using corn that came from the same source, placing the same number of kernels in the popper for each trial, and using the same popper for all trials.
6. It has thicker kernels and a higher water content.
7. How fresh the popcorn was could influence the outcome of the experiment. Stale, dried-out popcorn could show little difference from the variations. The starting temperature of the popper might also be important.

Student Activity Workbook

● H-22-1: STUDY GUIDE

1. Whether it is of interest to you.
2. Review topics studied in class, walk through a supermarket, or scan newspapers and magazines.
3. *Reader's Guide to Periodical Literature.*
4. Use the library's card catalog or computerized book list.
5. Take notes.
6. The United States Department of Agriculture and the Department of Health and Human Services.
7. To concentrate on one small area of the topic that you can study in depth.

8. Time, resources, equipment, space.
9. A proposed solution to a scientific problem.
10. So you know the point of your experiment and can develop a procedure that leads to meaningful results.
11. Give another person an idea of what the experiment is trying to prove.
12. How many variables you are going to consider.
13. To determine if results are valid.
14. Consistent results from several trials.
15. The format used all school year.

● H-22-2: NUTRITION AND YOU

1. Nutrition
2. molecular, whole
3. Department of Health and Human Services
4. the father of modern medicine
5. France
6. respiration
7. combustion
8. Magendie
9. Complex
10. much

● T-24: PARTS OF AN EXPERIMENT

1. title
2. hypothesis
3. procedure
4. questions
5. data table

● *Experiment* 22-1: PROPERTIES OF POPPING CORN

1. The popcorn dried in the dehydrator—the dehydrator had removed so much water there wasn't enough left to cause popping.
2. The fresh popcorn—no water had been removed.
3. In an airtight container to minimize water loss.

● *Experiment* 22-2: A TASTE OF TASTE TESTING

Answers will vary.

Chapter 22: Developing Experiments in Food Science

PARTS OF AN EXPERIMENT

TEXT PAGES 352–363

DIRECTIONS: Label each part of an experiment.

1. THE _____

—explains what the experiment is trying to show or prove.

2. THE _____

—gives a proposed solution to a scientific problem.

3. THE _____

—gives detailed directions for conducting the experiment.

4. THE _____

—identify the information you hope to discover by doing the experiment.

5. THE _____ _____

—organizes data in a useable format.

TEXT PAGES 364–373

SUGGESTED TIME SCHEDULE

180-day course—4 days.
90-day course—2 days.

STUDENT OBJECTIVES

- Evaluate whether a career in food science or related fields would be right for you.
- Identify career areas open to people with college degrees in food science and technology.
- List careers available to people with college degrees in home economics or a related field.
- Discuss the duties of a dietitian and the settings in which a dietitian might work.
- Differentiate between commercial and noncommercial establishments in the food service industry.
- Compare and contrast entry–level and higher–level jobs in the food service industry.

CHAPTER SUMMARY

- Because of the various branches of food science, there are many career opportunities in this field.
- Food scientists and food technologists have college degrees and work to apply science and engineering to various aspects of food production and processing.
- A wide variety of careers are available to those with a college degree in home economics or a related field.
- A dietitian combines food and nutrition with food management to help people in a variety of settings eat healthy diets.
- Opportunities in the food service industry fall into two areas—commercial and noncommercial.

- The amount of education and training people have affects whether they are qualified for an entry–level job or a higher–level job in the food service industry.

BACKGROUND INFORMATION

This final chapter of *Food Science* surveys some of the many career options available in the areas of food science and technology, food and nutrition, and the food service industry. These career options include a wide range of positions. Some require extensive education and training while others have no educational or experience requirements.

Students graduating from college with degrees in food science are earning some of the highest beginning salaries in the country. Unfortunately, not many high school students are aware of this when choosing a career. Students who are interested in or skilled in science should be aware of the career opportunities in food science before they enter college.

Teacher's Resource Guide

ACTIVITIES

1. Introduce students to the wide variety of careers in food science, food and nutrition, and the food service industry. Discuss the training and skills needed for the various positions.
2. Invite a food scientist to speak to the class about careers in food science. Possible community industries that might employ a food scientist would include a milk processing plant, a canner, or a freezing or drying operation.

3. Arrange a tour of a local food processing plant or the food science research facilities at a nearby college or university.

4. Obtain information from the closest college or university that offers a major in food science. Have students investigate the entrance requirements and what a course of study in food science at that institution would include.

5. Invite a home economist employed in the food industry to speak on opportunities for home economists in various aspects of the food industry.

6. Invite a local vocational school or community college instructor to speak to the class about the programs offered in the area of food and nutrition.

7. Invite a panel of people who work in the food service industry to speak to the class. Panel members could include someone from a fast-food restaurant, someone from a full-service restaurant, someone from a buffet-style restaurant, someone from the school cafeteria, and someone from a hospital or industrial cafeteria. Topics of discussion could include similarities/differences and advantages/disadvantages of these settings, education and experience required for various positions, opportunities for advancement, etc.

8. Have students read and discuss the following article: "One School Where the Final Exams Are Easy to Swallow," *Smithsonian*, December 1984, page 121. This article gives an excellent description of the Culinary Institute of America.

9. Have students interview two people who work in careers related to food. Use **H-23-2: Interview Guidelines** to help students plan and conduct their interviews.

ANSWER KEY
Student Text

● ANSWERS TO QUESTIONS IN TEXT:

p. 370

1. The National Livestock and Meat Board and the National Dairy Council are private organizations that provide nutrition education.

2. People studying to be teachers of physical education, home economics, and some areas of science, as well as medical doctors, dentists, and nurses all study nutrition in college.

● CHECK YOUR FACTS

1. Ensuring an adequate, acceptable, and safe food supply.
2. The production, packaging, distribution, preservation, evaluation, and utilization of food.
3. To experiment with food products to decide which ones can be taken into space and how they should be packaged.
4. Food editor of a magazine, home economist for a supermarket chain, demonstrator for a food company, food or nutrition researcher, college instructor, dietitian, or Cooperative Extension agent.
5. They combine food and nutrition with food management to help people eat healthy diets.
6. Hospitals, schools, industries, and city health departments.
7. In full-service restaurants, fast-food chains, and buffet-style restaurants.
8. Those for which no experience or advance training is needed.
9. They plan and control financial resources to serve nutritious, safe, and appealing meals at a cost consumers can afford.

● CRITICAL THINKING AND PROBLEM SOLVING

1. By developing and utilizing energy-efficient systems for the development, processing, and marketing of food products.
2. To select meals that stay appetizing in appearance, won't spill easily, and are safe to eat when kept at a given temperature for a period of time.
3. To get quality food as economically as possible.
4. Answers will vary.
5. Answers will vary.
6. Answers will vary.

● H-23-1: STUDY GUIDE

1. A college degree.
2. Good taste, appeal, and nutritional value.
3. Soybeans.
4. To ensure that no harmful bacteria or other contaminants are present.
5. Home economics or a related field.
6. To see how diet affects performance.
7. Food management.
8. They teach people how to control medical conditions through diet.

9. Commercial and noncommercial.
10. Entry-level jobs.

● H-23-2: INTERVIEW GUIDELINES

Answers will vary.

● H-23-3: NUTRITION AND YOU

1. Teaching of physical education or home economics, medicine, dentistry, and nursing all require course work in nutrition.

2. Some private food companies employ nutritionists to promote nutrition education.
3. Pay attention to the credentials of anyone giving information on nutrition.
4. Nutritionists communicate basic information about the importance of food choices to health.
5. Following sensible eating habits is one of the best ways to be and stay nutritionally healthy.
6. Answers will vary.
7. Answers will vary.
8. Answers will vary.
9. Answers will vary.